D0992436

James Monroe

Good Neighbor Boy

Illustrated by Maurice Rawson

James Monroe

Good Neighbor Boy

By Mabel Cleland Widdemer

the NEW *Bobbs-Merrill* COMPANY, INC.
® AN ASSOCIATE OF HOWARD W. SAMS & CO., INC.
Publishers · INDIANAPOLIS · NEW YORK

COPYRIGHT © 1959, THE BOBBS-MERRILL COMPANY, INC.

ALL RIGHTS RESERVED

PROTECTED UNDER UNIVERSAL COPYRIGHT CONVENTION

AND PAN-AMERICAN CONVENTION

LIBRARY OF CONGRESS CATALOG CARD NUMBER: 59-12854

PRINTED IN THE UNITED STATES OF AMERICA

For David Laurance Chambers, with admiration and deep appreciation; Laurence Gouverneur Hoes, great-great-grandson of President James Monroe, with grateful thanks for his valued and helpful advice; Dr. James Monroe Jones, friend and physician.

U. S. 1130956

Illustrations

Full pages

Numerous smaller illustrations

Contents

★ ★

Books by Mabel Cleland Widdemer

★ James Monroe

Good Neighbor Boy

The Snakebite

It was a bright October day in 1765. Mrs. Spence Monroe and her seven-year-old son, Jemmy, were standing on the doorstep of their home in Westmoreland County, Virginia.

"I wonder what can be keeping your father," said Mrs. Monroe. "He left before sunrise, and now it's late in the afternoon."

The Monroe home stood in a clearing in the forest. In front of the house there was a broad lawn. To the left of the lawn stretched tobacco fields, bare now because it was fall. Around the clearing the forest stood like a protecting wall.

As she watched for her husband, Mrs. Monroe

noticed how beautiful the forest was. A strong wind shook the branches of the golden beech trees, the red oaks and the tall dark pines. The swamp maples flamed like bonfires.

Jemmy's mother was worried. "Your father should be home by this time," she said.

"It takes a long time to track down a wolf," young Jemmy reminded her.

"I know, and I hope he catches it," said Mrs. Monroe. "It's the first wolf we've had around here in a long time."

"Look!" cried Jemmy suddenly. He pointed to an opening in the forest. "There's Father now! He's been hurt!" He ran toward his father. Mrs. Monroe was close behind him.

"Spence!" she called. "What happened?"

Mr. Monroe tried to smile. "It's just a snake-bite, Elizabeth," he said.

"A snakebite!" she cried. "Oh, Spence, that's dangerous." She turned to Jemmy. "Go and get

12

Black Feather," she ordered. "Tell him to bring his snakebite medicine as fast as he can. Hurry!"

Jemmy ran toward the forest. Black Feather was an old Indian. He was one of the last of the tribe that once had owned all of the land in this part of Virginia. His home was a hut on the bank of the Potomac River, and he made his living by trapping animals and catching fish.

Mean and thoughtless boys often sprung his traps after he set them. They cut his fish lines. So Black Feather didn't like boys—any boys. He had threatened to do terrible things to any that he caught near his hut.

Jemmy's parents had forbidden their children to go near the Indian. "Mother must have forgotten," thought Jemmy, as he ran toward Black Feather's hut. "Father must be very sick to make her forget."

When he came in sight of Black Feather's hut, he slowed down. Black Feather was sitting

13

peacefully in front of his hut. He looked harmless, but Jemmy was afraid to go any nearer.

"I must go on," he told himself. "I must give him Mother's message." He called up all his courage and walked bravely toward the old Indian.

As soon as Black Feather caught sight of Jemmy, he leaped to his feet. He let out a yell that made Jemmy shiver. Then he rushed forward and caught the boy by the shoulders.

"Black Feather catch you at last," he shouted, as he started to pull Jemmy toward the hut. "You bad boy who springs traps and cuts fish lines."

Jemmy tried to free himself. "No, no," he said. "I never have bothered your traps or fish lines. Listen! My father, Spence Monroe, has been bitten by a snake. My mother wants you to bring your snakebite medicine right away."

Black Feather loosened his grip as soon as he heard the name. "Spence Monroe," he repeated. "You Spence Monroe's son?"

"Yes," said Jemmy.

"You not bad boy," said Black Feather. "Spence Monroe good friend of mine. He say he told you not to bother Black Feather."

"That's right," said Jemmy.

"You brave boy," said the old Indian. "You not afraid of Black Feather. You help father. Now Black Feather help, too."

He hurried into his hut. When he came back,

15

a deerskin bag hung over one of his shoulders. "Good medicine here," he said, patting the bag. "Pocoon sure cure for snakebite. White man call it bloodroot. Father better soon. We go now."

They started off together, but in a little while Black Feather stopped and looked down at Jemmy. "You too slow," he said. "Legs too short. Black Feather go on. You follow."

He turned and soon was out of sight.

By this time the sun was a red ball of fire, sinking in the west. The wind whistled through the treetops. The first star of evening appeared.

Jemmy trudged on alone. It was almost dark in the forest now. The trees met over Jemmy's head. Thick, tangled bushes and vines grew close on either side of the narrow trail. As he went along, Jemmy heard a strange rustling sound in the underbrush.

"It's only a rabbit," he told himself. But the sound grew louder. No rabbit ever made that much noise. Maybe a large animal was coming through the underbrush. Jemmy remembered that his father had been tracking a wolf that very day.

Maybe that same wolf was here in the forest! Jemmy's heart began to pound wildly.

"I wish I had my gun," thought Jemmy. Last April, on his seventh birthday, his father had given him a gun. Already Jemmy was a good shot. He often went hunting with his father.

But he didn't have his gun, and he was a long way from home. It had grown so dark that he could hardly see the trail, but he started to run.

Then he tripped on a tree root. Down he went, headfirst. His knees and the palms of his hands hurt. He thought he must have skinned them. He lay still, trying to catch his breath. The noise seemed to be coming nearer.

Suddenly a tall man on horseback rode out of the shadows. He saw Jemmy just in time and

pulled his horse to a stop. He swung out of the saddle quickly and bent over the boy.

"Are you all right?" he asked.

Jemmy couldn't say a word, but he nodded. Then he got to his feet.

"What's your name?" asked the man.

18

"James Monroe," Jemmy said, "but everybody calls me Jemmy. I like that better."

"Isn't it rather late for you to be out in the forest alone?" the man went on. "If you tell me where you live, I'll take you home."

"I live at Monroe Hall," said Jemmy. "This trail leads right to it."

The man lifted Jemmy into the saddle and swung up behind him. "My name is George Washington," he said pleasantly. "I'm visiting my brother who lives at Wakefield Plantation."

Jemmy almost fell off the horse. Why, George Washington was a hero!

"I've heard about you," said Jemmy. "My father says you and the other American soldiers won the war against the French and the Indians."

George Washington laughed. "Not quite," he said modestly. "Remember, there were British soldiers fighting with us, too."

Jemmy nodded. "I know. But the British didn't know how to fight the Indians, as the Americans did. They wanted to fight standing up and out in the open. My father says that their red coats and white breeches made fine targets."

"So they did," George Washington said seriously. "The British wouldn't listen when we told them that. They wouldn't believe us until many of their men had been killed."

"My uncle, Judge Jones, says the British laughed at the Americans. They laughed because our soldiers didn't have fine uniforms and special guns. But we showed them who were the best soldiers."

"We knew how to fight the Indians because we had been doing it for years," said George Washington. "The only way we could protect our homes was to fight in the Indian way. We learned to hide behind trees and bushes, and to load our guns while lying down.

20

"The British didn't know anything about this kind of fighting," he went on. "We can't blame them too much for wanting to fight the way they had been trained to fight."

Jemmy liked George Washington. This man was fair. He tried to see how other people felt.

They rode in silence for a little way. Then George Washington said, "We should go faster. Could you hold on if we galloped?"

"Yes, sir!" Jemmy answered. He grabbed a handful of the white horse's silky mane and dug his knees into its smooth sides.

Away they went like the wind! It was wonderful! Jemmy never had had such a ride.

"I see you like a fast horse, too," George Washington said when they pulled up in front of the Monroe home.

Jemmy slipped to the ground. He held up his hand. George Washington shook it gravely.

"Thank you for bringing me home," Jemmy

said. "And thank you for helping to win the war against the French and Indians."

"You are welcome," George Washington smiled. "I am glad to have met you. I hope our paths cross again some day, Jemmy."

Jemmy watched George Washington wheel his horse and gallop across the clearing. He watched until the trees shut off his view. He was proud to have met such a great man.

When Jemmy went inside, he saw at once that Mr. Monroe was much better. He was propped up in a chair with his leg resting on a stool. Black Feather was squatting beside him. The Indian turned when Jemmy entered the room.

"Father fine now," he said. "Black Feather got here quick without short legs."

Halloween

"AN EAST wind never blows anybody any good," grumbled Sele, the Monroe's Negro cook. She was cross because her fire wouldn't burn. She put more wood on it, then puffed out her cheeks and blew hard. A cloud of smoke billowed into the room. Sele coughed and sputtered.

Her daughters, Mima and Rachel, were peeling potatoes. They coughed and sputtered, too. So did Jemmy and Ralph. Ralph was Sele's youngest child. He was seven, just Jemmy's age. He and Jemmy played together most of the time. Now they were playing soldiers in one corner of the kitchen.

Mr. Monroe had whittled two sets of wooden pegs to look a little like soldiers. Today Jemmy was playing that he was George Washington. His pegs were American and British soldiers. Ralph's were French and Indians.

"Ouch!" cried Mima. She threw down her knife. It had slipped and cut her finger.

"Didn't I tell you the east wind always brings trouble?" said Sele.

"Oh, Sele, I've cut my hand when there wasn't any wind at all," laughed Jemmy.

Sele shook her head. "See here, Mister Jemmy," she scolded. "Don't tell me I'm wrong."

At that moment Jemmy's eleven-year-old sister, Elizabeth, came into the kitchen. She was a pretty girl, with blond hair and blue eyes like Jemmy's. Her face was round and rosy, while Jemmy's was long and thin. Elizabeth laughed easily. Jemmy had a good sense of humor, too, but he didn't laugh so easily as Elizabeth did.

24

"What did Jemmy do to make you cross, Sele?" asked Elizabeth.

"He says I'm wrong," Sele answered. "I said that Mima cut her finger because the wind is from the east. An east wind always brings evil spirits. Jemmy says that isn't true."

"I doubt that the east wind has much to do with evil spirits," said Elizabeth. "If there are any around, it's because of Halloween."

"Halloween!" Sele cried. "Why, I'd forgotten about Halloween."

She turned back to the fire. It was burning brightly now. Delicious smells were beginning to come from the pots that hung from the black iron crane over the flames. The best smell of all was coming from the oven, which was built right into the brick fireplace. Sele was baking bread.

Sele settled herself comfortably on a wooden bench, where she could watch the fire. "Would you like to have me tell a Halloween story?"

"Please do," the children begged.

"Well," she began, "when I was a little girl, my big sister Milly and my little brother Sammy and I lived with our Mama and Papa on a big plantation."

"That was before you came to live with us, wasn't it?" Jemmy asked her.

"Long before, honey," Sele nodded. "One Halloween Mama had to leave us children while she worked at the big house. It was a mean night, just like tonight. The east wind shook the door and whistled down the chimney. It blew and whistled as if it was trying to get in!

"Milly and Sammy and I sat close to the fire. Mama had given us some apples and chestnuts to roast. But the fire wouldn't burn right, and we were afraid to go to the woodpile for more wood. We were even afraid to look at the dark corners of the room. We remembered all the stories Mama had told us about ghosts and goblins on Halloween. We were sure there were ghosts hiding in the darkness all around us!

"Our old black cat was sitting near by, but she wasn't watching the fire. She was watching the door, and her big green eyes never blinked. She seemed to be watching and waiting for someone. We were sure she was waiting for a witch to take her riding on a broomstick.

"For a long time the cat didn't move. She just sat there, watching and waiting. Suddenly we heard a noise outside, a long 'who-oo-oo.' The old cat jumped up, waving its tail.

"You can bet Milly and Sammy and I were scared! We sat there as close together as we could get, and we watched that old cat walk to the door. 'Miaow!' she went. 'Miaow! Miaow!' She looked back at us as if she wanted us to open the door. But we wouldn't move.

"Then we heard the noise again, 'who-oo-oo, who-oo-oo,' and something tapped on the window. Milly and I screamed and grabbed hold of each other. Little Sammy started to cry.

"Suddenly the door flew open with a loud bang. A gust of wind blew out the fire and filled the room with smoke. 'Who-oo-oo! Who-oo-oo!' The noise was right in the cabin now."

Sele paused. Ralph let out a little shriek and hurried to his mother's side. Elizabeth looked worried, and even grown-up Mima and Rachel looked frightened.

Only Jemmy wasn't afraid. "Who opened the door?" he asked calmly. "It couldn't have been a ghost or a witch."

Sele threw back her head and laughed. "I declare, Mister Jemmy, you have more sense than all the rest of these children together." She glanced scornfully at her daughters. "Of course it wasn't a ghost or a witch. It was Mama! She'd brought us some goodies from the big house!"

Laughter filled the kitchen. Sele went back to her work. She stirred the food cooking in the pots, and added salt and pepper. She took a pan of beautiful brown bread from the oven. "Get some more wood, Ralph," she said.

"Who, me?" Ralph pretended he hadn't heard right. The woodpile was out in the yard, and he didn't want to go out there. It was dark, and the wind was sighing mournfully through the trees.

"Yes, you," Sele nodded. "Hurry!"

Ralph moved slowly toward the door. Jemmy

saw that he was frightened. "Come on, Ralph," he said. "I'll go with you."

The wind swooped in when they opened the door. It made the candles flicker and the fire smoke. Rachel sprang to close the door.

Outside, black rain clouds moved swiftly across the sky. The woodpile seemed far away. Jemmy and Ralph ran across the yard.

As they were filling their arms with wood, they heard a mournful cry, "Who-oo-oo!"

"It's—it's a ghost, Mister Jemmy!" Ralph cried through chattering teeth.

"It's only a hoot owl," Jemmy said. He didn't want Ralph to know that he was scared, too.

"Look!" Ralph pointed with a shaking finger. Something white had just come from the forest. It was hurrying toward them.

That was enough for Ralph. He dropped his wood and ran for the house. Jemmy was close behind him, but he held on to his armful of

wood. Sele needed wood, and he wasn't going out to that woodpile again tonight!

They rushed into the house and slammed the door. "A ghost! A ghost!" Ralph cried.

"What are you talking about?" Sele demanded. She was sorry she had told that story.

Jemmy dropped the wood into the box, then turned to Sele. "Something dressed in white came out of the forest," he told her.

Just then there was a rap on the door.

"That's it!" Ralph screamed. He dived under the table in the middle of the room. Mima, Rachel and Elizabeth were already there!

The rap sounded again.

Sele grabbed the poker and went to the door. She wasn't going to let anything hurt her family. Jemmy picked up a piece of wood.

"Who's there?" Sele demanded.

"Black Feather," was the answer.

Sele flung open the door. The old Indian

stepped inside. He was wrapped in a white blanket. In one arm he carried a package wrapped in deerskin.

"For you," he told Jemmy.

He drew his hunting knife and cut the thongs that bound the package. "For you," he repeated. It was a wolf pelt. It had been nicely cured and was ready to be used as a rug.

"Me kill wolf for your father," Black Feather explained. "It not bother him again. Father say you want fur rug for cold feet next winter. So Black Feather bring."

Jemmy stroked the soft fur. "Thank you very much, Black Feather," he said.

"Indians like brave people," Black Feather said. "You brave boy." He threw a scornful glance at the girls and Ralph huddled under the table. Then he stalked out.

Jemmy lay awake for a while after he went to bed that night. He smiled to himself, thinking of

Sele's story. It hadn't really frightened him. He knew there were no such things as ghosts.

But he had to admit that he had been scared when he heard the hoot owl out by the woodpile and saw the figure in white coming from the forest.

How kind Black Feather was to bring him the wolf pelt for a rug beside his bed! He leaned over and gave it a gentle pat. It was going to feel good under his bare feet next winter. Jemmy closed his eyes and went to sleep.

The Mysterious Package

ONE DAY Mr. and Mrs. Plunkett arrived from Boston. Before they had moved to Boston, the Plunketts had lived in Virginia, near the Monroes. The two families were good friends, and now Mr. and Mrs. Plunkett had come back for a visit.

Sele's husband, Cato, carried in their luggage. Jemmy and Ralph helped with the smaller bags and packages. Jemmy noticed that one package he carried into the house smelled delicious.

Mr. Plunkett saw Jemmy sniffing the package and laughed. "That's something we brought you from Boston," he said. "We hope you'll like it.

U. S. 1130956

We brought a little gift for everyone. Shall we wait until after dinner?"

Jemmy thought dinner would never end. Mr. and Mrs. Plunkett had two servings of everything.

At last Jemmy was sure that even stout Mr. Plunkett couldn't eat another mouthful. But he did. "I'll just have one more biscuit," he said, "with a bit of butter and some honey."

Jemmy watched every bite he took. He itched with impatience. At last Mr. Plunkett put the last crumb into his mouth. "Best food I've tasted since we left Virginia," he said.

"Now you must rest from your long journey," Mrs. Monroe said.

"An excellent idea," said Mrs. Plunkett. "Our trip was very tiring."

Jemmy watched the Plunketts go up the stairs. Had his mother forgotten? Mr. Plunkett had said they would open the presents after dinner.

Mrs. Monroe saw his disappointment. She put her arm around his shoulders. "Run off and play for a while. The presents will still be here when you return."

With a sigh Jemmy went off to find Ralph, but Ralph seemed to have disappeared. At last he saw Rachel coming across the lawn.

"A ship from England just docked," she said. "Ralph went to watch the unloading."

The Monroes lived in the part of Virginia between the Rappahannock and Potomac rivers. Many plantations were located on one or the other of these rivers. Ships from England could sail upriver to the planters' own wharves or docks to load and unload their cargoes.

A creek flowed across the Monroe plantation and emptied into the Potomac River. Big ships could sail a little way up the creek, but not as far as the Monroe plantation. They stopped at a wharf where the deep water ended.

Jemmy hurried along the path that followed the creek to the wharf. It was fun to watch the unloading. Everyone came from near and far. Some people came to watch, others to pick up whatever they had ordered from England. Most things came in boxes or barrels.

The long wharf was crowded. Jemmy dodged in and out among the people, looking for Ralph. He tried to remember to be polite and say "Excuse me" whenever he bumped into someone. He was especially sorry when he stepped on the foot of a tall gentleman dressed in handsome clothes.

The man was Mr. Richard Henry Lee. He was a rich planter who lived in a beautiful house called Chantilly. He was a friend of Jemmy's father.

"I'm glad to see you, Jemmy," he said. "I have someone I want you to meet." He called a boy who was watching a man roll a barrel down the narrow gangplank. "Come here, Harry. I want you to meet James Monroe. Jemmy, this is Harry Lee, my cousin's son."

Jemmy liked Harry at once. He was about two years older than Jemmy, and was handsomely dressed in the latest London style.

For a moment Jemmy felt shy. He knew that the Lees were rich. They could order things from England that Jemmy's parents couldn't afford. Harry's fine clothes made Jemmy's suit seem very plain. His mother had made it from cloth woven on the Monroe plantation.

Harry smiled and held out his hand, and Jemmy's shyness disappeared.

"Harry is visiting my brother at Stratford Hall," Mr. Lee explained. "There are few boys of his age around here. I hope that you two will be friends."

Jemmy smiled. "I'm sure that we will."

"I have some business to attend to," Mr. Lee said. "Meet me here in an hour, Harry."

The two boys watched the tall figure disappear in the crowd.

"Let's find a better place to watch the unloading," Jemmy suggested. "Let's climb up on those big barrels. Then we can see over everybody's head." He pointed to a row of hogsheads lined up on the wharf near the ship.

When they were settled on top of one of the hogsheads, Jemmy went on, "I like to guess what's in the boxes." He pointed to one that a man was carrying on his shoulders. "Maybe there's coffee or sugar in that one."

"Or jewels and silks," suggested Harry.

Jemmy hadn't thought of such expensive things. Most of the things that the ships brought to the Monroe family were for everyday use. The Monroes were not so wealthy as some of their neighbors.

Once there had been a special box, Jemmy remembered. It had contained a roll of silk for a dress for his mother and a handsome cloth coat with silver buttons for his father. Best of all, it had contained sweetmeats.

Jemmy's mouth watered as he remembered the wonderful taste of the candied lemon peel, dried ginger and rock candy.

Jemmy knew that special box had arrived because the tobacco crop had been good that year. Mr. Monroe had been able to send more hogsheads of tobacco to England than usual. So he had been able to buy extra things, like the fine coat, the silk and the sweetmeats.

Both boys knew that tobacco was hard to grow. They knew that the seed had to be sowed early in March in some protected spot.

It took the seeds a little while to sprout. During that time the field hands were busy plowing and raking the tobacco fields.

When the tiny plants were ready to be moved from the seedbeds to the fields, everyone helped with the work. On the Monroe plantation, even Sele left her cooking to help. The work had to be done quickly, because the plants had to be transplanted before they grew too big.

Even if the spring planting went well, the summer might bring trouble. Hawk moths came to lay eggs on the broad green leaves. The eggs hatched into worms that ate the leaves. Jemmy and Ralph often helped the field hands pick these worms off the plants.

Jemmy hadn't forgotten that Ralph was supposed to be at the dock, too. He stood up on the hogshead to look around. When he saw Ralph, he shouted, "Ralph! Here we are!"

Ralph came running over. He looked disappointed. "There's nothing for us," he said.

"Maybe there'll be something on the next ship," said Jemmy. "Anyway, remember that we have packages at home to open when Mr. Plunkett wakes up."

Ralph's face brightened. "That's right," he said. Then he ran off whistling happily.

By and by the crowd thinned out. Even the sailors left the ship to spend a few welcome hours on land. The boys walked to the end of the wharf to get a better look at the ship.

"I'm going to cross the ocean in a ship like that some day," said Jemmy. "I'm going to visit England and France, and maybe Spain."

"That would be fun," Harry agreed.

"I wonder what it's like on board," said Jemmy. "Let's go and see."

As the boys started toward the gangplank, they heard someone calling them. It was Mr. Lee. "I've been looking for you," he said. "Have you had a good time together?"

"Wonderful," answered the boys.

"We were just going to board the ship to look around," added Jemmy.

Mr. Lee shook his head. "I'm afraid that will have to wait until another time. I have finished my business and must go home now."

A Negro servant was waiting near by, holding the Lees' horses. The boys said good-by, and Harry and Mr. Lee jumped into their saddles.

"Jemmy, you must pay Harry a visit while he

is staying at Stratford Hall," said Mr. Lee. Then he and Harry galloped away.

Jemmy looked around for Ralph, but couldn't see him. Then he remembered the presents that were waiting to be opened. He wondered what could be in the mysterious package that smelled so good. He hurried home as fast as he could.

The Monroes and the Plunketts were waiting when Jemmy got home. Even Andrew, the baby, was in Mrs. Monroe's arms. The gifts were on the table.

"Ladies first," Mr. Plunkett said. He handed Mrs. Monroe a package with a handsome bow.

Mrs. Monroe gasped when she unwrapped a beautiful scarlet cloak. "Oh, how lovely," she exclaimed.

Mrs. Plunkett smiled. "I was glad when you admired my cloak this morning," she said. "I knew then you'd like our gift for you."

Next Mr. Plunkett gave Elizabeth a package.

She took so long to open the package that Jemmy began to fidget. If it were his package, he'd have it unwrapped in a jiffy.

"Oh, thank you," Elizabeth cried at last. She held up a big doll. "It's beautiful."

"Now, Jemmy," Mr. Plunkett said at last. He handed Jemmy a package. Jemmy sniffed, but this wasn't the package that had smelled so good. He opened it quickly. There were four strange-looking sticks in it. Jemmy was puzzled. He never had seen anything like them before.

"They are a new kind of pencil," Mr. Plunkett explained. "They were made in Germany by a man named Faber. Two of your pencils have black lead, and two have red."

"I've heard of the new pencils," Jemmy said, "but I've never seen any before. Thank you, sir."

He was pleased, but the pencils reminded him that he would soon be having lessons. Mr. and Mrs. Monroe had sent for a young Scottish clergyman to come to teach their children. They were expecting him any day.

There was a wooden horse for five-year-old Spence, and a monkey on a stick for little Andrew. For Mr. Monroe there was a silver snuffbox made by a man named Paul Revere.

Sele, Mima, Rachel and Ralph had slipped into the room. Cato and the field hands were standing in the doorway. There were gifts for all of them.

There was only one package left now. As Mr. Plunkett picked it up, Jemmy moved closer. This was the mysterious package that smelled so good.

The package contained a wooden box. Mr. Plunkett lifted the lid, and a delicious odor filled the room. When Jemmy saw what was in the box, his face fell. Whatever it was, it looked like pieces of dried brown mud.

"Help yourself," Mr. Plunkett said. "It's chocolate, made by Mr. John Harmon of Dorchester,

Massachusetts. It's said to be the first chocolate ever made in America."

Jemmy broke off a big piece and put it in his mouth. Surely anything that smelled so good must taste good, too. The next moment he was sorry that he had taken so much. It was bitter! He wished he could get rid of it, but of course he couldn't. He let it melt in his mouth, and at last he was able to swallow the sticky mess.

Elizabeth had watched him. She took only a little piece. "It's nice," she said politely. But Jemmy knew that she didn't like it, either.

Mr. and Mrs. Monroe were polite about the pieces they took, but they didn't seem to like the taste. Spence took as big a piece as Jemmy's. A moment later he spit it out. Mrs. Monroe was angry. "Spence Monroe! Where are your manners?" she demanded. "Please leave the room."

Mr. Plunkett saw that no one really liked the chocolate. He looked so disappointed that Jemmy felt sorry for him. "May I have more?" he asked.

"Of course! Take all you like," Mr. Plunkett said, beaming with pleasure.

Jemmy took two big pieces. Mrs. Monroe opened her eyes in surprise. Surely Jemmy couldn't have liked the chocolate that much!

Jemmy ran to the kitchen. He broke the chocolate into small pieces and gave a piece to Ralph, Rachel, Mima and Sele.

Sele made a face when she swallowed hers. "Are you trying to poison us?" she cried.

Jemmy explained that Mr. Plunkett had brought the chocolate all the way from Massachusetts. "I know it tastes bitter," he said. "Maybe it would be better if it had some sugar in it."

Sele was interested at once. "Give me some," she said. Jemmy gave her all he had.

Sele put the chocolate in a pot and hung the pot on the crane over the fire. Then she added sugar and let it all melt together. She tasted it. It still wasn't right. She added milk and stirred and tasted again. This time her face lighted up. "Try that!" she commanded.

Jemmy tasted it. "It's good!" he cried.

This gave him an idea. "Sele," he said. "Let's surprise Mother and the Plunketts."

He got some more chocolate from Mr. Plunkett, who was delighted to give it to him. Then he had Sele make a big pot of the hot chocolate. "Now," he said, "serve this instead of tea this afternoon."

When Sele set the large silver tea tray on the table that afternoon, she was shaking. Suppose her mistress didn't like the chocolate!

Mrs. Monroe picked up the silver teapot and began to fill a pretty china cup. She was astonished when a steaming brown liquid came from the spout instead of tea! "What is this, Sele?" she demanded.

"Taste it!" Jemmy begged. "Mother, please taste it before you say anything."

Mrs. Monroe took a careful sip. "Why, it's delicious!" she exclaimed.

"It's the chocolate with sugar and milk added to it," Sele said. "It was Mister Jemmy's idea."

Everybody had a cup of hot chocolate. It was delicious. Now Mr. Plunkett's gift was much appreciated, and he was very happy.

Little Girl Lost

A FEW days later the Monroes were eating dinner. "How I miss the Plunketts!" Mrs. Monroe said. "The house seems empty without them."

Suddenly there was a knock at the door. Rachel opened it and brought a man into the dining room. His face was white with worry. Jemmy recognized him as the man who had just moved into the neighborhood. His name was Hitchcock.

"Have you seen my little daughter, Anne?" Mr. Hitchcock demanded. He was too upset to be polite. "We can't find her. My wife is so worried that she is almost out of her mind."

52

"Sit down and tell us about it," Mr. Monroe said. He pushed a chair forward and Mr. Hitchcock sank down on it. Mrs. Monroe motioned to Rachel to bring him some hot tea.

"Anne is four," Mr. Hitchcock said. "She was playing in the clearing around our house. There's a lot to be done around our place still, and my wife was busy. She didn't look out to see what Anne was doing for quite a while. When she did look, she couldn't see Anne.

"My wife thought maybe the child was hiding somewhere just to tease her. But she searched the woods around the clearing and Anne wasn't there." Mr. Hitchcock was so upset he couldn't say any more.

"If Anne is only four, she can't have gone very far," Mr. Monroe said. "I'll get my servants and we'll help look for her."

Mr. Hitchcock shook his head. "We're afraid that Indians may have taken her."

"We haven't had any trouble with Indians for many years," Mr. Monroe said quickly. "Not in this part of Virginia. There aren't enough Indians left around here to bother us."

"We had plenty of trouble with them where we lived beyond the mountains," said Mr. Hitchcock. "That was one reason we moved. I've seen one old Indian——"

"That's Black Feather," Mrs. Monroe interrupted. "He wouldn't take your little girl."

"I don't trust Indians," Mr. Hitchcock said.

"Didn't I hear that your indentured servant ran away a few days ago?" Mr. Monroe asked.

"Yes, he ran away three days ago," Mr. Hitchcock replied. "We had an argument and I lost my temper. We've thought of him, too." He rose wearily from his chair. The short rest and the tea seemed to have made him feel a little better. "Thank you," he said. "I must go back to my wife."

54

"I'll call my servants," Mr. Monroe said. "We'll search the forest."

"I'll go stay with Mrs. Hitchcock," Mrs. Monroe decided. "It will be hard for her to wait for news alone."

Cato saddled Mrs. Monroe's horse, and she rode off down the trail.

When she had gone, Jemmy told Ralph about Anne. "Let's go look for her," he said.

"But Mister Jemmy, we're not supposed to go into the forest," Ralph said. "Your mother wouldn't like it if we did. Mine wouldn't either."

Jemmy hesitated. "That's right," he said. "I'd almost forgotten that."

"I don't want to go there anyway," Ralph went on. "It's swampy and scary. There are snakes and goodness knows what else in there."

"Y-e-e-s, there probably are," Jemmy said doubtfully. "But what about the little girl? We'd hate to be lost in there ourselves, and Anne's only four." Jemmy remembered how frightened he had been the night George Washington had found him.

"We'll go," Jemmy decided. "I'm sure Mother would want us to help."

He hurried along the trail toward the Hitch-cock farm. Ralph followed unwillingly. When they drew near the clearing, the boys left the trail. It was hard going through the forest. Gnarled roots and tangled vines caught at their feet. Sharp spines of berry vines caught at their hands and clothes, trying to hold them back.

Presently the ground grew swampy. Big frogs croaked and dived out of sight as the boys came close. A snake slid from a rock where it had been sunning itself.

"I don't like it here," Ralph said. "It's awfully dark and spooky."

"Let's go a little farther," Jemmy said.

They hurried on. The ground grew wetter

and softer underfoot. Suddenly Ralph tripped
over a thick vine and staggered forward. He
caught hold of an overhanging branch, but not
before he had stumbled up to his knees in thick
black mud.

"Help, Mister Jemmy! The swamp's got me!" he shrieked. He struggled to free himself. The more he struggled, the deeper he sank.

Jemmy was scared, but he didn't want Ralph to know it. He had heard stories of cattle getting stuck in the muddy swamp and never getting out. He had to think of some way to get Ralph out of the mud before he sank deeper.

The branch Ralph clung to was bending lower and lower. It looked as if it might break at any moment, leaving Ralph to sink in the mud.

"Don't be scared!" Jemmy said. "I'll get you out." But he didn't see how he could.

He looked around. He saw a stout vine just out of reach of Ralph's hands. "If I can get that to Ralph before the branch breaks," he thought, "he can hang onto it."

Jemmy began to climb the tree from which the vine was hanging. He moved carefully. He mustn't fall and get caught in the swamp, too.

58

Then they'd never get out. He crept out on the limb and reached for the vine. He swung it closer and closer toward Ralph. "Catch it!" he commanded.

Ralph was afraid to let go of the branch. He was so scared his teeth were chattering. "Catch it!" Jemmy shouted again.

Timidly Ralph stretched out one hand and reached for the vine. The branch creaked as he moved. His fingers touched the vine, lost it, then caught it again. At almost the same moment the branch broke with a loud *snap!*

"Get a good grip on the vine," Jemmy said. He slid down the tree. There was another vine growing along the ground. He grabbed its loose end and threw it to Ralph. "Pull yourself along that," he cried, "and I'll pull from here."

Slowly, inch by inch, Ralph pulled himself along the vine. Jemmy tugged with all his strength. Suddenly, with a loud sucking noise,

Ralph was free. Jemmy grabbed him by the arms and pulled him out on solid ground.

Ralph lay down. He was worn out. His legs and feet were covered with mud. His hands were sore. "I'm not going another step!" he said.

Jemmy didn't blame him. He didn't want to move either. What if they had both been caught in that sticky black mud?

Then Jemmy heard a rustling in the bushes. He jumped to his feet. Ralph shut his eyes and lay still. He was sure this was the end!

Jemmy wished he had brought his gun. There must be a wild animal of some sort prowling near by. Jemmy didn't like being without protection. Then he heard the noise again, louder and closer. He picked up a stick and threw it with all his might in the direction of the sound.

A man's voice cried, "Ow." The tangled vines and underbrush were shoved aside roughly, and Black Feather sprang into view.

60

"Why you throw stick?" he demanded angrily, rubbing his head.

"I'm sorry!" Jemmy exclaimed. "I thought an animal was making the noise. I wanted to scare it away."

"What you doing here?" the Indian asked.

Jemmy told him about Anne and how he and Ralph had been trying to find her. "Now we're lost ourselves," he ended.

Black Feather helped Ralph to his feet. He scraped off the mud with a stick. "Follow me," he ordered and started through the swamp.

Jemmy and Ralph kept close behind him. They were afraid to let the Indian out of their sight. If they did, they might never find their way home again.

Suddenly Black Feather stopped. He motioned to the boys to be quiet. Not far ahead, through the trees, they saw a man with a child in his arms. He stood looking around doubtfully. At last he took a few steps in one direction. Then he stopped and took a few steps in another direction. When he turned back, Jemmy saw his face.

"It's Mr. Hitchcock's indentured servant and Anne," he whispered. "He's lost."

Black Feather nodded. The indentured servant looked tired and thin. Anne was sleeping peacefully with her head against his shoulder.

"Hey!" Jemmy shouted. "You've found Anne!"

The man almost dropped the child. He stared at Jemmy in surprise. "Jemmy Monroe!" he exclaimed. "How did you get here?"

"We were looking for Anne, but we got lost," Jemmy replied. "Black Feather found us. He's taking us home. You'd better come along."

"I will indeed!" the man said. "I'm lost, too. I've been hiding in the forest for three days. A little while ago I found Anne. I wanted to take her home, but I couldn't find my way."

62

Black Feather grunted and held out his arms. The man placed Anne in them.

"Thank you," the man said. "I couldn't have carried her much farther."

"Follow me," Black Feather commanded.

The servant, whose name was Brawn Wood, held back. "Will the Hitchcocks have me punished if I go back?" he asked Jemmy.

"No," Jemmy said. "You found Anne, and you were trying to take her home, weren't you?"

"Yes," Brawn Wood nodded.

"Then they'll be so grateful they'll forgive you," Jemmy said. "Come along."

Black Feather was almost out of sight by now. They stumbled along behind him as fast as they could. At last they came to the clearing in front of the Hitchcock house.

Mrs. Hitchcock had been watching at the window. "They've found Anne!" she cried and flew from the house. Mrs. Monroe and Mr. Hitch-

cock came running behind her. He had come
home to see how his wife was getting along.

Mrs. Hitchcock clasped Anne in her arms.
She was crying "Anne! Anne!"

Mr. Hitchcock looked at Black Feather and
Brawn Wood angrily. Then he turned to Jemmy.
"Where did you find Anne, and why are these
two with you?" he wanted to know.

"Brawn Wood found her in the swamp and
got lost trying to bring her back," Jemmy said.

"Ralph and I got lost, too, and Black Feather found us. He found Brawn Wood and Anne while he was bringing us back. So you can thank Brawn Wood and Black Feather."

"Well, I seem to have been wrong," Mr. Hitchcock said. "I thought Brawn or the Indian had taken Anne." He turned to the indentured servant. "I owe you an apology, Brawn, and many thanks." He held out his hand and Brawn took it.

Mr. Hitchcock turned to Black Feather. "I owe you an apology, too, Black Feather," he said.

"Black Feather never hurt little girl," Black Feather said indignantly. Then he turned on his heels and disappeared into the forest.

Jemmy and Ralph were afraid that they would be scolded for going into the swamp. But Mrs. Monroe was too proud of Jemmy to scold him. Sele didn't scold Ralph, either. She washed off the mud and gave him a hot supper and put him to bed.

Trouble
in the Land

JEMMY was awakened one night by the sound of voices downstairs. He jumped out of bed and went to the door of his room. The floor was cold. February was already more than half gone. As he opened the door, he heard the voices again. He wondered what was happening.

A half dozen men were gathered around Jemmy's father near the fireplace. His mother's brother, Judge Joseph Jones, was talking to Richard Henry Lee. Beside Mr. Lee was a tall man whom Jemmy never had seen before. He was speaking as Jemmy slipped into a shadowy corner of the room.

"The Stamp Act is unfair," the tall man said in a smooth, pleasant voice. "The British Parliament has no right to pass such a law. It has no right to tax us against our wishes."

"That's right, Patrick," Judge Jones agreed. He turned to Jemmy's father. "Mr. Henry made a fine speech about the Stamp Act in the House of Burgesses not long ago. He said that only the men we have elected should tax the people of Virginia.

"Some people didn't like the speech. They said it was treason, disloyalty to England. 'If this be treason,' Patrick said, 'make the most of it!' It was a thrilling moment. I was proud to be there and hear him."

Jemmy knew that the House of Burgesses made the laws in Virginia. His uncle, Judge Jones, was a member of the lawmaking group. Other members came from different parts of the colony of Virginia.

"Mr. Henry is right," Richard Henry Lee said. "We don't send people to represent us in the British Parliament. But Parliament tries to tell us what to do. We should protest against the Stamp Act. I suggest that we hold a meeting in Leedstown soon. Let's ask all our friends to attend. Then we can talk the problem over and decide what to do."

The others agreed. As he listened to them, Jemmy tingled with excitement. He wished he were a man. Then he could go to Leedstown, too. It made him angry to think that England was treating the colonies so badly.

Patrick Henry and Judge Jones went on talking about the Stamp Act. Jemmy had heard his father speak of it before, but he didn't know much about it. Now he wanted to hear more. What was it? Just what had it done to make his father and all his friends so angry? Jemmy wished he knew.

He strained to hear better. But the others were talking, too, and drowned out Patrick Henry's voice. Jemmy moved out of his corner, closer to the fireplace. He wanted to hear!

Suddenly Mr. Henry turned from the fire and saw him. "Upon my word!" he laughed. "What have we here, a patriot in a nightshirt?"

"Jemmy!" Mr. Monroe cried sternly. "What are you doing down here? You're supposed to be in bed!"

"Y-yes, Father," Jemmy stammered. "I heard voices, and I came down to see what was going on. Then I heard you talking about the Stamp Act and Parliament and—and I wanted to hear more."

"I think we do have a patriot here," Patrick Henry said. "A real one."

"So it seems," Jemmy's father replied, smiling. "I think most of you know my son, James. Jemmy, this gentleman is Mr. Patrick Henry."

Patrick Henry shook Jemmy's hand. "So you want to learn more about our troubles with Parliament," he said. "Why, may I ask?"

"My father says all Americans should be interested in the Stamp Act," Jemmy said seriously. "And I'm a good American."

"Then Patrick Henry is the man to talk to you," said Judge Jones. "He can tell you more than anyone else here."

Mr. Henry put his arm around Jemmy's shoulders. "Sit here by the fire and get warm, Jemmy," he said. "I'll tell you more about the Act."

When Jemmy was settled comfortably, Mr. Henry went on. "The Stamp Act was passed last March by the British Parliament. It says that all American colonists must put special stamps on marriage licenses and many other kinds of documents, or papers. Without these stamps, the documents are not lawful. The money we pay for the stamps goes to the English government.

"We Americans don't like the Stamp Act. We wouldn't mind so much if we had had people to speak for us in Parliament. Then we would have had something to say about it. But we weren't allowed to have anyone there to represent us.

"We Virginians aren't the only ones who object to the Act," he went on. "People in all the colonies are objecting."

Jemmy sat thinking for a moment. He loved his father's plantation, which the Monroes had

71

owned for more than a hundred years. When he thought of Virginia, he thought of his own home. When he thought of America, he thought of Virginia. Somehow a wrong to America was a wrong to Virginia, to his family and to him.

"Father, could I go to the meeting in Leedstown with you?" he asked. "Could I watch you hold your meeting? I'd like to learn still more."

The men looked at one another and smiled. "Good boy!" Patrick Henry said.

Jemmy could tell from the twinkle in his father's eyes that he was pleased. "May I, Father?" he repeated. "Please let me go."

"I think that might be arranged," Mr. Monroe said with a broad smile.

A few days later, early in the morning, Mr. Monroe shook his sleeping son gently. "Wake up, Jemmy. Wake up if you want to go to Leedstown."

Jemmy rolled over on his back and rubbed his

eyes. He felt like going back to sleep, but he sat up instead. How cold it was in the room!

When Mr. Monroe was sure that Jemmy was awake, he left the room. Jemmy stepped out of bed. The fur rug that Black Feather had given him felt warm and soft under his bare feet. He dressed quickly.

Big bowls of steaming porridge and smoking hoecakes were waiting on the breakfast table. Through the window Jemmy saw Cato walking up and down with White Star, Mr. Monroe's favorite horse. Ralph was behind him with Jemmy's horse, Jasper.

Once he had eaten something, Jemmy began to enjoy the day. It was going to be exciting to ride to Leedstown in the crisp February air.

There had been a sleet storm during the night. The trees and bushes were covered with ice. They sparkled like diamonds.

"White Star and Jasper look as if they were

smoking," Jemmy laughed. He pointed to the white clouds of steam coming from their nostrils.

Jemmy and his father had all they could do to hold the horses to a trot. The crisp cold air made them want to gallop. But Leedstown was ten miles away, Mr. Monroe pointed out. The horses mustn't tire too quickly.

Leedstown was a small place, but it was important in that part of Virginia. Many ships from England docked there. They brought fine furniture and china, beautiful clothing, and many other things. Some people said that Leedstown would be as big as Philadelphia some day.

The sun was high overhead when Jemmy and his father finally came to Leedstown. The spire of a white church shone in the sun. Mr. Monroe pointed to the inn near the church. "That's where we're having the meeting," he said.

There were only two rings left at the hitching rail in the stable yard of the inn.

Mr. Monroe was pleased. "We're having a fine turnout," he said as he tied his horse to one of the rings. "It's larger than I had hoped for."

Mr. Monroe looked proud as he walked toward the door of the inn. The crowd proved that there were many patriots in Virginia. These men had come from all parts of the county.

"You must take care of yourself now, Jemmy," Mr. Monroe said. "I shall be busy."

Jemmy was disappointed. "Couldn't I watch some of the meeting, Father?" he asked.

"I'm sorry, son." Mr. Monroe put his hand on Jemmy's shoulder. "The meeting today is for men only. After it's over, I'll introduce you to some people you've never met before—the Washingtons and more Lees. But for the present you'll have to wait. You can find something to do, can't you?"

Jemmy turned away. Maybe Mr. Richard Lee had brought his young cousin, Harry.

Jemmy had seen Harry only once, that day on the wharf. It would be fun to see him again.

Jemmy peeped through the diamond-shaped windowpanes of the room where the men were meeting. He could see that the room was crowded, and he recognized some of his father's friends. But Harry wasn't there.

Jemmy turned away, disappointed. He started to cross the stable yard. He saw a stone on the ground and kicked it along before him. His head was bent, and his eyes were on the stone.

"Better watch where you're going or you'll have a cold bath," someone said suddenly.

Jemmy looked up, surprised. A dark-haired, dark-skinned boy stood there, smiling.

"Thank you," Jemmy said, smiling, too. "I didn't even see the trough." The boy didn't look like an American, Jemmy thought.

"My name is Peter Francisco," said the boy. "What's yours?" Peter didn't speak like an

American either, Jemmy noticed. He had a strange way of saying words. Jemmy liked it.

"I'm James Monroe. I came to Leedstown with my father this morning," he answered.

"I came with Judge Anthony Winston," Peter said.

Jemmy was glad to find someone who was his own age. "What can we do?" he asked. "I'd like to go to the meeting, but my father says I can't."

Peter thought a moment. Then he smiled. "There's a back stairs from the kitchen up to the second floor," he said. "We could follow the hall upstairs to the head of the main stairs. I'm sure we could see and hear from there."

Jemmy looked doubtful.

"We wouldn't be in the way there," Peter said. "They wouldn't even see us."

"We-e-ll, I would like to see what they do." Jemmy hesitated a moment longer, then decided. "All right, let's do it."

The two boys ran to the back of the inn. They looked through the window into the big kitchen. In one wall there was a huge fireplace, where the meals were prepared. It was like the fireplace at home, Jemmy thought, but much larger. Fire-blackened pots, with food cooking in them, hung over the flames. Shiny pans hung from the walls. A big table stood in the middle of the room. But nobody seemed to be there.

Carefully the boys opened the door and slipped inside. The kitchen was warm and full of the odors of cooking food. Beyond a closed door on the far side of the room, some men were talking. The stairway was on the right, opposite the fireplace.

Quietly but quickly the boys went to the stairway. It was dark, even in the middle of the day. They tiptoed up to the head of the stairs.

"Now where?" Jemmy whispered, looking curiously down the hall.

"There's a short hall at the end of this one," Peter said. "It leads to the main stairs. We can hide behind a railing there. Come on."

The boys crept noiselessly along the hall. Suddenly Peter stopped and motioned to Jemmy to wait where he was. Peter inched forward and peered around the corner. Then he crept back.

"There are two men hiding behind the railing," he whispered. "What can they be doing?"

Jemmy crept forward to look.

The two men were whispering together. "The tall man is Richard Henry Lee, of Chantilly," one of them said.

"H-m-m," the other man muttered. "He's a member of the House of Burgesses, too."

Jemmy almost gasped aloud. The men were spies! He must warn Father and the others! But how? He crept back to tell Peter.

"What shall we do?" Peter wondered.

"You slip down the back stairs and go around

to the front of the inn," Jemmy whispered. "Tell my father or Judge Winston—or somebody—that there are spies up here. I'll stay and watch. If the men try to get away, I'll yell or something."

Peter hurried down the back stairs. Jemmy crept forward to have another look at the spies. He peered around the corner. At that moment one of the men looked back.

"There's a boy back there!" the man hissed.

Jemmy was frozen with fear. Then, as the man sprang toward him, he shouted: "Spies, Father, spies! Upstairs! Quick, somebody, help!"

Things happened quickly after that. The men rushed toward the back stairs. Jemmy fell back. There were shouts from below and the sound of feet pounding on the stairs. That was all Jemmy remembered.

When he opened his eyes again, he was in bed in one of the rooms in the inn. His father and his uncle, Judge Jones, were smiling down at him. Peter Francisco and Judge Winston were on the other side of the bed.

"What—what happened?" Jemmy wanted to know. "How did I get here?"

"The men knocked you down when they tried to run away," his father said. "But we caught them."

"And chased them out of town," Peter added with a laugh.

Mr. Monroe ordered some food for the boys. Then he and the other men went downstairs.

After a hearty meal, Jemmy and Peter sat before the fire. Jemmy told Peter about his home. He told him about his mother and his sister and his brothers. He told him about Sele and Ralph. He even told him about Black Feather.

"Now tell me about your family," he ended.

Peter's dark eyes grew sad. He shook his head. "I don't have any family of my own," he said. "I live with Judge Winston and his wife."

82

"You mean you don't have a father and mother?" Jemmy asked in surprise.

Peter stared sadly at the fire. "I don't know who they were, or where I came from."

At that moment Mr. Monroe and Judge Winston came into the room. "The meeting is over," Mr. Monroe said. "We can go home now, boys."

"We'll ride part way with you," Judge Winston said. Jemmy was delighted. He liked Peter and was glad to spend more time with him.

The stableboy brought the horses to the door. Jemmy was surprised to see snow on the ground. It creaked under the horses' hoofs as the men and boys rode along.

"You boys must never forget today's date," Mr. Monroe said. "From now on, February 27, 1766, will be an important date in the history of Virginia. Today we Virginians—one hundred and fifteen of us, anyway—signed an important paper. We said that it is our right to be taxed only by our own representatives. We protested against the Stamp Act. And we agreed to do all we can to prevent its enforcement."

Soon Jemmy and Peter grew restless, jogging along in front of their elders.

"I'll race you!" shouted Jemmy.

"Beat you!" cried Peter, and off they went.

"Our sons seem to have become good friends today, don't they?" Mr. Monroe said.

"Peter isn't my son," Judge Winston said. "I wish he were. I found him one day wandering around the wharf at City Point."

"Poor lad," Mr. Monroe said. "Who were his parents? What happened to them?"

"That's a mystery," Judge Winston replied. "Peter is foreign, as you've probably noticed. I think he must be Spanish or Portuguese, but I'm not sure. He couldn't speak any English when I found him, so he couldn't tell me much.

"I did learn that some sailors brought him ashore from a large ship that had entered port a few days earlier. They put him on the wharf. Then they rowed back to their ship and sailed away.

"Peter was dressed in expensive clothes. There were silver buckles on his shoes, with the initials P.F. on them. But nobody knew who he was or why he had been put ashore at City Point.

"After he had learned a little English, he told

85

me about his home. It must have been a beautiful place, like a palace. His mother was a pretty woman, he said, gay and always laughing. He had a sister, who was younger than he.

"One day, he said, some men came into the garden where he and his sister were playing. They put a sack over his head and carried him away. When they took the sack off, he was aboard the ship that carried him here. That was all he knew.

"When I heard his story, I felt sorry for him. He was a nice child, well-mannered and quick to learn. I couldn't find out anything about his family. So my wife and I adopted him. He has done well, but I wish he had children of his own age to play with. I'm glad he and your son have become friends."

"Your story interests me," Mr. Monroe said. "I wonder who his parents could be?" He was silent for a moment. Then he went on, "It's too bad we live so far apart. Jemmy needs friends, too, and he seems to like Peter very much."

The men stopped at a fork in the road, where the boys were waiting for them.

"Jemmy won," Peter said. He was pleased to have his new friend win. Jemmy hadn't boasted as some boys would have done.

"Come and see me some time," Jemmy said. "We can go squirrel hunting."

"That would be fun!" Peter exclaimed.

Mr. Monroe and Jemmy waited until the Judge and Peter had ridden out of sight. Then they turned their horses toward home.

Mr. Monroe told Jemmy Peter's story.

"I like Peter better than any boy I know except Harry Lee," Jemmy said. "I wish he lived nearer. We could have fun together."

"I wish so, too," Mr. Monroe said.

New Things
to Learn

IT WAS almost dark when Jemmy and his father reached home. But it wasn't too dark to see that something was happening. Cato was leading a strange horse toward the barn. Ralph was trying to carry a big box into the house. A slender young man was just going through the front door.

"The Reverend William Douglas must have come!" Mr. Monroe exclaimed. He touched spurs to his horse and galloped across the clearing.

Jemmy followed slowly. He wasn't so pleased that the young clergyman from Scotland had come at last. It meant that school would begin. Jemmy wouldn't be able to play with Ralph or wander over the countryside. He would have to spend his time studying his lessons instead.

William Douglas was six feet tall. He had sandy hair and eyelashes, and the bluest eyes Jemmy had ever seen. He had a million freckles and spoke with a strong Scotch accent.

"I can't understand a word he says!" Jemmy told his mother. "How can I learn from him?"

"You will soon get used to his speech," Mrs. Monroe said with a smile.

By the time supper was over, Jemmy found that his mother was right. Already he could understand the young minister much better. Jemmy liked Mr. Douglas, too. Lessons might not be so bad after all.

Jemmy wished that there was someone his own age living near by—someone like Harry Lee or Peter Francisco. It would be nice to have someone share his lessons. Spence was too young. He hadn't even learned his ABC's yet.

Mrs. Monroe had taught Elizabeth and Jemmy to read and write and to do a little arithmetic. But Mr. Douglas was going to teach Jemmy Latin and Greek. There would also be lessons in history, geography and botany. Botany was the study of plants and flowers, Jemmy's mother had told him. He might enjoy that, but he didn't know about Latin and Greek.

Elizabeth was lucky. She just had to study more reading and writing. If girls knew how to spin and sew and sing, that was education enough.

The next morning Mrs. Monroe called Jemmy early. He pretended not to hear her. He rolled over and buried his face in the soft feather pillow. He didn't want to get up.

"You must set a good example for Elizabeth and Spence," his mother told him. Jemmy wished his mother didn't always expect him to set an example. It would be nice if Elizabeth or Spence was expected to do it once in a while.

The young minister asked the blessing at the breakfast table. It was longer than the one Jemmy's father used. When the family sat down at last, Mr. Douglas smiled at the children. "Ready for lessons?" he asked.

Jemmy wanted to shout, "No!" But he just sat there and ate his breakfast.

Mrs. Monroe understood how he felt. "I think lessons in the morning will be enough for today, Mr. Douglas. Jemmy can show you around the plantation after dinner. We're quite proud of it."

Mr. Douglas was a good teacher. He soon had Spence learning his ABC's from a hornbook.

Spence was proud of this hornbook. It was a wooden paddle with a sheet of paper pasted on it. The alphabet, the Lord's Prayer and verses from the Bible were printed on the paper. A thin sheet of transparent horn covered the paper. "That's how it got its name," Mr. Douglas explained.

The young minister spent most of the morning testing Jemmy and Elizabeth. He was pleased with them. "Your mother is a good teacher," he said.

Short as the school hours were that first day, Jemmy grew tired. He wasn't used to sitting still. His feet went to sleep. He stamped them to wake them up. Spence pretended that his feet were asleep, too. He stamped and stamped.

Mr. Douglas didn't say anything. He just looked at the boys. His look made Jemmy feel foolish. Jemmy stamped a little less loudly. After a while he stopped. Spence stopped, too.

If there had been something to look at besides blank walls, Jemmy wouldn't have been so tired. But the schoolroom was empty except for Mr. Douglas' desk and a bench and table for the children. It wasn't really a schoolroom, just a storeroom that Mrs. Monroe had had cleaned out. But it would have to do. There was no real school anywhere near the Monroes.

Mr. Douglas admired the Faber pencils that Mr. Plunkett had given Jemmy. "They'll be fine for writing in your copybook," he said.

He handed each of the older children a copybook. A copybook was made from large sheets of paper, carefully sewed together. "Be careful of these," he said. "Paper is scarce and mustn't be wasted." He handed each of them a small slate. "You can do your sums on these, not in your copybooks."

Mr. Douglas took from his pocket the largest watch Jemmy ever had seen. "We have time to learn a few rules on how to behave," he said. Then he opened a book and read:

"Never sit down at the table until asked, and always after the blessing.

"Ask for nothing. Wait until it is offered.

"Bite not the bread, but break it. Take salt only with a clean knife. Dip not the meat in salt. Hold not the knife upward, but sloping.

"Look not earnestly at any other who is eating. When moderately satisfied, leave the table. Sing not, hum not, wriggle not."

Here Mr. Douglas looked at Jemmy. Jemmy had wriggled at the breakfast table that morning. Mr. Douglas read on:

"Speak not unless you are spoken to.

"Say not, 'I have heard it before,' if anyone tells a story. Never endeavor to help him out if he tells it not right."

Mr. Douglas rose to his feet. "That will be all for today," he said. "Remember that I shall expect you to follow the rules I have just read."

At dinner that day Mr. Monroe said, "The foxes have been after our chickens again. Mr. Hitchcock has been having trouble, too. We

94

thought we'd go after them tonight. Would you like to join us, Mr. Douglas?"

"I'd be glad to," Mr. Douglas said.

Jemmy squirmed in his chair. He forgot the rule that said it wasn't polite to wriggle at the table. He forgot the rule about not speaking unless spoken to, as well.

"May I go, Father?" he begged. "I've been practicing, and I can shoot pretty well now."

"I think you may, son," Mr. Monroe said. "That is, if your mother agrees."

"Of course he may go!" Mrs. Monroe said. She wanted Jemmy to learn how to take care of himself.

"I can shoot as well as Jemmy," Elizabeth said. "Why can't I go, too? Boys have all the fun."

"You couldn't go through the woods in all those petticoats and skirts," Jemmy said.

"If you weren't so mean, I could borrow some of your clothes," Elizabeth said.

"Children! Children!" Mrs. Monroe cried. "No quarreling at the table!"

"Well, I could go if Jemmy would lend me something and you'd let me," Elizabeth pouted.

She looked as if she were going to cry. Suddenly Jemmy felt sorry for her. He knew how disappointed he would have been if his parents had refused to let him go. Elizabeth was right. She could shoot as well as he could. His clothes would fit her, too, for he was big for his age.

"Let her come, Mother," he said. "I'll lend her some clothes and look after her."

"I'll look after myself!" Elizabeth declared. But she gave him a grateful look.

"You'll soon be a young lady," Mrs. Monroe said. "Then you won't want to go fox hunting. There will be other things to interest you. So go now while you can enjoy it. If Jemmy and your father and Mr. Douglas are with you, I know nothing will happen to you."

96

"Thank you, Mother! Thank you, Jemmy!" Elizabeth cried. Jemmy felt good. Girls belonged at home. But, if it made Elizabeth happy to go, he was glad that he had taken her side.

The moon was high in the sky when the hunting party started out. Its light made the night nearly as bright as day. Mr. Hitchcock and another neighbor, Mr. Brown, joined them.

Mr. Douglas dropped back with Jemmy and Elizabeth. "What are your father and Mr. Hitchcock and Mr. Brown carrying in those sacks?" he asked.

"Fish heads," Jemmy told him. "They don't smell very nice, do they? But the foxes like them. Just wait and see."

At the edge of Mr. Monroe's cornfield, everyone stopped. The men opened the sacks and dumped the evil-smelling fish heads in a pile. "Now we'll hide in those bushes over there," said Mr. Brown.

The smell of the fish heads was strong on the night air. Before long a half dozen sleek red foxes appeared from the shadows.

"Hold your fire," Mr. Monroe whispered as Jemmy lifted his gun. "There may be more."

He was right. In another ten minutes four more foxes had come to feast on the fish heads.

"All right, fire!" Mr. Monroe commanded.

Jemmy took aim, but he was too excited to hold his gun steady. He fired and missed. Each of the men hit a fox. So did Elizabeth. Jemmy was the only one who missed. He was disappointed, almost in tears.

"Some of the foxes got away, but it was a good night's work," Mr. Monroe said. "Now you children must get home to bed."

The fox hunt was over. Jemmy plodded along beside Elizabeth, carrying her fox. He was ashamed. After all his practicing, he hadn't been able to hit anything.

Elizabeth put her arm around him. "Don't be discouraged, Jemmy," she said. "You'll get one next time. Just wait and see."

Both children were tired. They had kept up with the men at the beginning of the evening. Now they walked more slowly. The men didn't notice that Jemmy and Elizabeth were falling behind.

Once Jemmy stopped to shift Elizabeth's fox from one hand to the other. It seemed to grow heavier with each step he took.

Then Elizabeth stopped. "I have to sit down for a while," she said. Jemmy's boots were heavy and hurt her toes.

"Just for a minute," Jemmy said. "We mustn't let Father and the others get too far ahead."

Just then they heard a noise close beside them. Jemmy whirled and leveled his gun.

Elizabeth sprang to her feet. She was afraid. "Wh-what is it, Jemmy?" she whispered.

"I don't know," he muttered. "I can't see anything. Can you?"

They heard the noise again. It came from shadowy bushes off to the right. It sounded as if something were moving. Suddenly the quiet was broken by a growl. The growl rose higher and ended in a shrill "*Yang-yang-yang!*"

Elizabeth screamed, and a cold chill ran down Jemmy's spine. Without thinking, he aimed his gun at the bushes and pulled the trigger. There was another scream and a wild thrashing in the bushes. Then everything was still.

Mr. Monroe and the other men came running back. They found Jemmy and Elizabeth huddled together in the path. Neither of them had moved. They were too scared. They were staring at the bushes with big round eyes.

Mr. Monroe approached the bushes cautiously. A moment later he shouted, "It's a big wildcat! Jemmy shot a wildcat!"

He came back, dragging the wildcat.

"That's one of the largest I've ever seen," Mr. Hitchcock said. "And look! Jemmy shot him right between the eyes. A fine shot, my boy!"

"I was lucky," Jemmy said with a shaky laugh. "I didn't even see him."

"You see, Jemmy," Elizabeth said later. "I told you your turn would come."

Everyone made a fuss over Jemmy that night. Sele brought him a plate of his favorite cookies and a big glass of milk. His mother hugged and kissed him. Spence looked at him with admiration. Elizabeth told the story over and over.

"Now you'll have another fur rug for your room," said Mr. Monroe.

"I think I'll give this one to Elizabeth," Jemmy said. "She doesn't have a fur rug." He didn't say anything more. But in his thoughts he added, "She didn't laugh when I missed the fox."

A Visit
to the Lees

THREE years had passed since Jemmy and Harry Lee had met on the wharf. Now Harry was visiting his father's cousin, Philip Lee, again. Mr. Lee thought that Harry might like to have some company, so he invited Jemmy and Elizabeth to spend a week at Stratford Hall, too.

When Jemmy and Elizabeth arrived, Harry came to greet them. Ten-year-old Jemmy was pleased to see that he was now as tall as Harry, who was two years older. His shoulders were broader, too.

"You're just in time for the fiddling contest," said Harry. "Come and join the fun."

A crowd had gathered on the lawn in front of Stratford Hall. Men, women and children formed a big circle around Mr. Overton, who managed the plantation for Mr. Philip Lee.

Mr. Overton stood on a platform. He held up a handsome three-cornered black beaver hat.

"This fine hat will be given as a prize to the best fiddler," he said. "All of you men and boys who own your own fiddles can be in the contest. Don't borrow anyone else's fiddle, please. Come up on the platform two at a time. Hurry now."

Two men climbed onto the platform.

"You first," Mr. Overton said. He pointed to an elderly man, who tucked his fiddle under his chin and began to play.

"He's good," Harry said when the first fiddler finished playing.

"I wish Ralph could play," Jemmy said. Ralph had come with Jemmy and Elizabeth to Stratford Hall. He was to look after them.

"Does he play better than that?" Harry asked. The second man had started a rollicking tune.

"I've never heard anybody play so well as Ralph does," Jemmy said simply.

"If he could borrow a fiddle somewhere, he could get into the contest," Harry said.

Jemmy shook his head. "No. The rule is that you have to have your own."

"Then he shall own one!" Harry declared suddenly. He disappeared into the crowd. Jemmy and Elizabeth looked at each other. What did Harry mean?

When Harry returned, he had Ralph with him. Harry had a fiddle under his arm.

"Ralph doesn't believe I want to give him my fiddle," Harry said. "Make him understand. I want to give it to him so he can enter the contest."

Jemmy stared at Harry. "A fiddle costs a lot of money. Do you want to give yours away?"

"Yes, I do!" Harry said. "Take it, Ralph. Get

in line before it's too late." He thrust the violin into Ralph's hands and gave him a push. "Hurry up," he said. "The fiddle's yours."

Ralph touched the violin gently. He ran his hand over the smooth wood and fingered the strings. Then he took his place at the end of the line. He was the last to be called.

"He's scared," Elizabeth said. "Suppose he gets so scared he can't play?"

"He'll be all right when he gets started," Jemmy said. "Wait and see."

"His knees are shaking!" Elizabeth exclaimed.

"He does look awfully scared," Harry said.

Ralph *was* frightened. He looked down into the faces of the crowd. There must have been a hundred people watching and waiting for him to begin. Every tune he knew seemed to leave his head. He stood there looking miserable.

Jemmy pushed his way to the front of the crowd. He caught Ralph's attention. He whistled the opening notes of one of Ralph's favorites. The music rushed back into Ralph's head. He lifted the violin and shut his eyes. He imagined he was back home, playing for the people he knew. The music poured from his fiddle.

Before he had finished, people were cheering and clapping. He had won!

"The prize goes to this boy," Mr. Overton said. He put the hat on Ralph's head. It came down over his ears. The crowd roared with laughter.

"I think it's a little too big for you," Mr. Overton smiled. "Maybe I should find a prize that's a little better for you."

Ralph clung to the hat. "This is what I want," he said stubbornly. "I want the hat!"

"But it doesn't fit," Mr. Overton said kindly. "Wouldn't you like something else?"

"I want to keep it," Ralph said again.

Mr. Overton was puzzled. "See here, boy," he said. "I'm not trying to take your prize away from you! I'm just trying to give you something that you can use yourself."

Tears shone in Ralph's eyes. He held on grimly to the hat and would not let go.

"What's the matter with him?" Harry asked. "Mr. Overton is right. The hat is too big for him."

Jemmy didn't like to see Ralph unhappy. He climbed up on the platform. He didn't think about the crowd watching him. He just wanted to help Ralph, whose shyness left him speechless.

"Why do you want to keep the hat, Ralph?" he whispered. "It *is* too big for you."

Ralph looked at Jemmy in relief. He could tell Jemmy. Jemmy would understand. "I want it for my pappy," he said. "He'd be mighty proud to wear this hat to church. He's never had anything but an old torn straw hat."

"He certainly would be proud!" Jemmy agreed. "I'll tell Mr. Overton why you want it."

Ralph drew a sigh of relief. He knew Jemmy would make it possible for him to keep the hat.

It was late afternoon of the same day. Elizabeth and Jemmy and Harry had had their dinner in the children's dining room. Now they had been asked to join their elders in the Great Hall.

"Don't stare so, Jemmy," Elizabeth whispered. "It isn't polite."

Jemmy had good reason to stare. He had never seen such a room. It was thirty feet long and thirty feet wide. It had a high ceiling and

109

hand-carved paneled walls. Its floor was so highly polished that he could see his reflection in it.

The door opened and a group of men and women entered. Now even fourteen-year-old Elizabeth stared. All the ladies had their hair dressed in the new style called the "tower."

First, their hair had been piled high in mountains of curls. Then the curls were greased and powdered and trimmed with all kinds of things. One lady had jewels in her hair, another ribbons and lace. Still another had feathers and flowers. But the lady who made Jemmy gasp had a small sailboat on top of her head.

"What would happen if she went out in the wind?" Jemmy whispered. He was too polite to laugh, but the lady did look funny. She had to hold her head stiff to balance the tower of hair with the ship on top.

"I guess they must spend hours with their hair-

dressers," Elizabeth sighed. She had been surprised at first, but now she envied the ladies. "I'm going to try to do my hair that way when I get home."

Just then Ralph entered the room, followed by two Negro men. Ralph carried the fiddle that Harry had given him. One of the men had a flute, the other a banjo. They took their places in a corner of the hall and began to tune up.

Jemmy was proud of Ralph. He had been asked to play for the dance with these men.

The ladies and gentlemen took their places for the dance. The gentlemen wore square-cut coats with turned-back cuffs and lace ruffles at their wrists and throats. Jemmy thought they looked very handsome. Their long, tight-fitting vests were made of beautiful satins and silks.

Some of the men wore white powdered wigs. Others, whose hair was longer, wore it tied at the back of the neck with a black ribbon.

112

Jemmy envied Elizabeth as Harry led her out to join the others. He wished he hadn't been so stubborn about taking dancing lessons. He felt left out as he stood watching the others.

He heard a voice behind him. He turned quickly. A girl about his own age stood there. "Don't you dance?" she asked in a friendly voice.

Jemmy shook his head. "No," he answered.

She was a plain girl. Her light brown hair was tied back with a red ribbon. Her white muslin dress was too large for her. She held up the skirt, which almost touched the floor.

"Mother always makes my dresses for me to grow into," she said. "By the time they fit, they're old." She smiled at Jemmy.

"My name is Maria Overton," she went on. "My father runs this plantation. I saw you this afternoon. Is that your sister with you? She's pretty. She dresses the way I'd like to. Her clothes fit her. What's your name?"

113

Jemmy told her.

"If you can't dance, you're wasting your time here," she said. "Let's go for a walk. I'll show you my pet raccoon. I think you'll like her. Some boys wouldn't. They would think it's funny for a girl to have a pet raccoon. Grownups think it's funny. They say she'll bite me, but she hasn't yet. Do you want to come with me?"

Jemmy and Maria slipped from the room and ran down the long stone steps to the garden. Maria led the way past the kitchen. Like Sele's kitchen at home, it was separate from the rest of the house. They passed the servants' quarters and the smokehouse. Maria pointed out the red brick house where she lived with her parents. At the foot of the vegetable garden, there was a large cage.

Two bright eyes peeped out at them. Two furry black hands grasped the bars of the cage. A small pointed face peered out.

114

Maria said, "I've brought a friend to visit you, Mehitable. Shake hands with him."

A small black paw came out between the bars. Jemmy shook it gravely.

"She likes you," Maria said. "If she didn't, she wouldn't shake your hand."

"Does she know any other tricks?" Jemmy asked. "I had a pet raccoon once. All it did was follow me around like a dog."

"What happened to it?" Maria asked.

115

"When it got older it went back to the forest. I never saw it again," answered Jemmy.

"I suppose that's what Mehitable will do some day," Maria sighed. "Yes, she knows more tricks. I've had her since she was a baby. She learns quickly. Raccoons are smart. She can play dead and walk on her front paws, too."

"My, she is smart!" Jemmy said.

"Wait! I'll take her out of the cage. Then you'll see," Maria told him.

She opened the door of the cage. She lifted Mehitable out and put her on the ground. "Play dead!" she commanded. Mehitable rolled over on her side and lay perfectly still.

A dog barked near by. "Oh, that Jason Mason has let his dog out again!" Maria cried.

She reached to put Mehitable back in her cage. But Mehitable had heard the yapping, too. Quick as a flash she was up a near-by tree. Jason Mason's dog came bounding across the vegetable garden. It reached the foot of the tree and put its paws on the trunk and barked shrilly.

"Go away!" Maria cried. "Don't you hurt Mehitable! Jemmy, do something! Chase him away or something."

The dog was jumping higher and barking more loudly, but Mehitable was safe. She sat on a limb watching the dog with bright little eyes.

Finally Jemmy said, "Don't worry, Maria. I'll get Mehitable down. Do you have a rope?"

"I'll get one," Maria said. She ran off and soon returned with a stout rope.

Jemmy tied one end around the dog's neck and the other end to a near-by tree. The dog tried to get free, but the rope held.

Jemmy climbed the tree after Mehitable. She was trembling when he brought her down to Maria. Maria put her back in her cage.

Then Maria and Jemmy ran back to Stratford Hall.

A Dangerous Criminal

THE NEXT day rain lashed against the windows of Stratford Hall. Jemmy and Harry didn't know what to do. They were outdoor boys and felt cooped up and restless in the house. They stood at the window staring out at the rain.

Someone knocked at the door of their room. "Come in," Harry called.

Ralph entered the room. His brown eyes were wide with excitement. "The sh-sheriff and his men are at the d-d-door," he stuttered as he began. Then he added, more slowly, "They're hunting an indentured servant who has run away from a plantation up the river."

118

"Why did they come here?" Jemmy wanted to know.

"They tracked him here," Ralph said. "The sheriff wants to search the buildings."

"Let's help look for him!" Harry exclaimed.

"The sheriff says he's dangerous," Ralph went on. "He escaped from prison in England. Somebody paid his way to America."

But Jemmy and Harry weren't listening any more. They were on their way to talk to the sheriff.

There were many indentured, or bound, servants in Virginia, the boys knew. They were people whose passage to America had been paid by somebody else. To pay for the journey, the bound servants worked without pay for a certain number of years. At the end of that time they were free.

The boys found the sheriff and his men at the back of the house.

"Do you think the man's hiding here?" Harry asked.

"We tracked him here," answered the sheriff.

"Come on, Jemmy!" Harry cried. "Let's look for him. He can't be far away."

"You boys stay out of this," the sheriff shouted after them. "He's dangerous, I tell you!" Jemmy heard him, but Harry already was racing up the narrow stairs to the Great Hall.

When they reached the Hall, the two boys stopped. "Where shall we look?" Harry asked.

"He won't be here," Jemmy said. "He won't be in the library or the drawing room or any of the bedrooms, either. He couldn't get up here without being seen. He must be hiding on the ground floor."

"Or in one of the outbuildings," Harry said.

"The cook would find him in the kitchen," Jemmy pointed out. "He couldn't be there."

"No, but he might be in the stable or the barn,"

Harry said, "or even in Cousin Philip's office. With guests in the house, Cousin Philip hasn't gone to his office today."

"We'd better start downstairs first," Jemmy said, "before the sheriff does."

The boys went to the schoolroom. It was empty. Then they went to the spinning room across the hall. Three Negro women were spinning and weaving cloth for the family's use. They were singing as they worked.

"Have you seen any strangers about?" Harry asked. He didn't want to scare them.

"No, sir," they said. They went back to their singing, which the boys had interrupted. The spinning wheels began to whir again.

"Let's try Cousin Philip's office now," Harry suggested. "It's closer than the other buildings."

The boys crossed to the office and slipped inside. The office was shadowy and cool. There were high bookcases filled with books, a tall desk, several chairs and a table. But there was no place for a person to hide.

"Let's try the stable," Harry said.

The stable was beyond the office. It was filled with a horsey smell that Jemmy liked. Many horses were out in the pasture, but some were in their stalls. They moved restlessly when the boys entered the stable. They seemed uneasy.

The boys looked in the empty stalls. They looked in the dark corners. They even looked in the stalls where the horses were standing. But they found nothing, nothing at all.

"That's strange," Jemmy said thoughtfully. "I was sure we'd find him here. This is the best place to hide. It's where *I'd* hide, at least."

They were standing beside a pile of straw near the door. Jemmy glanced at the straw, then tugged at Harry's sleeve.

"Look," he whispered.

Half buried under the straw on the far side of

the pile Harry saw a sleeve. He turned to the door. "Come on, let's tell the sheriff," he said.

The straw moved suddenly. "Don't do that!" a muffled voice said. A boy about sixteen climbed out. He was ragged and thin. He had

an ugly bruise over one eye and a bad cut on his upper lip. "Please don't call the sheriff," he begged.

Jemmy and Harry stared at the boy. "Are you the dangerous criminal?" Jemmy asked. "Did you run away from a plantation up the river?"

The boy nodded his head.

"What's your name?" Harry asked.

"Mickey Cook," the boy answered. "If the sheriff catches me, he'll take me back to Mr. Regan."

"Who is Mr. Regan?" Jemmy wanted to know. "Did he bring you to Virginia?"

Mickey nodded. "He was in court in London the day I was sent to jail."

"Why were you sent to jail?" Jemmy asked.

"I stole a loaf of bread because I was hungry," Mickey said. "Later I escaped from jail. Mr. Regan found me and remembered seeing me in the courtroom. He said he wouldn't turn me in.

He said he would pay my way to America if I would work for him.

"It sounded good then. I wanted to go to America. I thought it would be fine to have a place to work for the rest of my life. I wouldn't have to worry about where I would sleep or how I would get something to eat.

"Mr. Regan kept his promise. But he has been mean to me ever since. He doesn't give me enough to eat, and he beats me if I do something wrong. He said if I tried to run away, he would tell the sheriff I was a dangerous criminal."

Jemmy looked at the boy's thin face and tattered clothes. He felt sorry for him.

"Please don't tell the sheriff you found me," Mickey went on. "If I could hide here for a day or two, maybe Mr. Regan would give up looking for me." He sounded desperate and unhappy.

Jemmy and Harry looked at each other. "What do you think?" Harry asked.

"I don't know," Jemmy replied. "I'd hate to turn him over to the sheriff if Mr. Regan is that kind of man. But we'll be disobeying the law if we *don't* tell the sheriff. We don't have any right to hide a runaway servant."

"But if Mr. Regan beats him—" Harry began.

"It seems to me that it would still be wrong to hide him," Jemmy said.

"Just for a little while?" Mickey begged.

Jemmy hesitated. Then he said, "Suppose we hide him until the sheriff leaves. Then we'll tell your cousin. He'd be fair, wouldn't he?"

"That's a good idea!" Harry cried. "Cousin Philip would do the right thing."

Mickey looked relieved. "I wish I had a better place to hide," he said. "I'm afraid the sheriff will find me here."

The boys thought hard for a while. Then Harry snapped his fingers. "I know a place—if we can find it," he said.

"Where?" Jemmy asked. "We'd better hurry."

"There's a secret room somewhere in the attic," Harry said. "Years ago a carpenter found a spring under a board up there. When he pressed the spring, a door slid open. There was a secret room! If we could find that spring, Mickey could hide in the room."

"Doesn't your cousin know about the room?" asked Jemmy doubtfully.

"He doesn't believe the story," Harry said.

Mickey shook his head sadly. "It isn't much of a chance. First, I'll have to get to the attic without being seen. Then you'll have to find the room."

"We can get you to the attic," Harry said. "Wait here." He went outside and came back a few moments later. "There's nobody in sight," he said. "Let's hurry."

The boys slipped out of the stable. They went quickly around the office to the side door of the house. Once inside, Harry led them up to the attic.

"Now!" he said when the door had closed behind them. "Let's find that spring."

The attic was dark, but Harry had brought some candles. Their tiny flames threw flickering shadows on the walls as the boys hunted.

"It's hopeless!" Mickey said at last. "There isn't a loose board here!"

"We haven't looked behind those barrels and boxes yet," Jemmy said. He began to tug at the nearest box. "Come on!"

"Be quiet," Harry warned. "Somebody might hear us before we find the spring."

The boys set to work again. Before long, Jemmy lifted a loose board and found the spring! When he touched it, a door in the wall slid open. The boys peered into a small, brick-walled room.

"Why, it's part of the chimney!" Harry exclaimed. "Nobody will find you here, Mickey.

After the sheriff leaves, we'll take you to Cousin Philip."

"What about fresh air?" Jemmy asked. He was always practical about such things.

Mickey stepped into the room. "There are cracks between the bricks," he said. "I'll get plenty of air when the door is closed."

Jemmy and Harry closed the door and put the board back in place. They rolled a barrel in front of the door. Then they hurried downstairs.

The sheriff and his men were still searching the grounds and outbuildings. After an hour they gave up and went away. The boys met Cousin Philip in the hall and told him what they had done.

"Why didn't you tell the sheriff when he was here?" Cousin Philip asked sternly. "You know indentured servants must be returned."

"Yes, sir, we do," Jemmy said. "But we thought this was different. We don't think Mr. Regan has treated Mickey very well. He's awfully thin, and he's bruised and cut."

"Has he been beaten?" Mr. Lee demanded.

"We think so, sir," Jemmy said.

"Bring him to me," said Cousin Philip. "No man has the right to bully or mistreat an indentured servant. If Regan has beaten the lad, I'll see that he doesn't have to go back."

The boys hurried to the attic and brought Mickey down. Mr. Lee took one look at his thin face, his cut lip and the bruise over his eye. Then he was silent for a while. "Don't be afraid," he said gently. "Who did this to you?"

"Mr. Regan, sir," Mickey said.

Just then the door opened and Jemmy's uncle, Judge Jones, entered the room.

"Uncle Joseph!" Jemmy cried happily. If anybody could help Mickey, it would be his Uncle Joseph. He and Harry told Mickey's story again. The Judge listened carefully.

Then he patted Mickey on the shoulder. "Don't worry, lad. I know what to do."

"Who is this Regan?" Philip Lee asked.

"He runs the Taylor plantation up the river," Uncle Joseph said. "I know Mr. Taylor well. He won't stand for anything like this. When I tell him about Mickey, I'm sure he'll let Regan go. Mickey isn't the first person Regan has beaten, but this is the first time we could prove it. Now we have him where we want him. The country will be better off without him."

"What about Mickey?" Jemmy wanted to know. "What will happen to him?"

"I'll take him over," Judge Jones said. "I'll pay Regan for his passage to America. You won't mind working for me, will you, boy?"

Mickey's pale face was flushed with joy. "Oh, thank you, sir! I'd love that!" he cried.

Silver Heels

It was a bright autumn day in the following year. Squirrels were busy putting nuts away for the winter. The leaves had changed color and were rustling down like gentle rain. A crow cawed, and a dog barked far away.

Jemmy Monroe walked slowly through the tunnel the road made through the forest. The road was called Parson's Lane because it led directly to the Reverend Archibald Campbell's school. Jemmy carried his books under one arm. Over the other shoulder he carried his gun. This morning he wished he were going almost anywhere in the world except to school.

Early that morning his father had whistled for his dogs and gone partridge hunting. He had taken Spence and Ralph with him.

Standing at his window, Jemmy had watched them go with a sad heart. There had been many a morning when he had gone with his father.

Since that night of the fox hunt, Jemmy had become a good shot. On his eleventh birthday, last spring, his father had given him a fine new gun from London. Jemmy was very proud of it and cared for it as a prized possession.

Today, since he couldn't go hunting, he decided to carry his gun to school. Sele wanted to make a pigeon pie. He would try to get some pigeons for her on the way home.

Dr. Campbell's school was at his home. In addition to his own sons, he taught a dozen or so boys from neighboring plantations. He was a Scotchman who took teaching seriously. His school was well known. His students gained a

good knowledge of Latin and Greek and the great books written in those languages. They studied mathematics. They learned about loyalty, honesty, honor and devotion.

As Jemmy trudged toward the school, he was thinking. People said that it was fun to grow up. But he wasn't so sure. Was he luckier than Ralph or his brother Spence? They didn't have to go to school on such a beautiful day!

When Jemmy reached the school, Dr. Campbell was standing in the doorway, greeting his pupils. "Good morning, Jemmy," he said. "I see you're going hunting again. Put your gun away and find your seat."

Jemmy entered the schoolroom and went to his desk. There were two new boys this morning. One was sitting at the desk beside Jemmy's. He was tall, slender and dark-haired.

"My name's John Marshall," the boy whispered with a smile. "What's yours?"

Jemmy told him.

"I'm living with the Campbells while I go to school," John Marshall said.

"The Parson taught my father, too," he went on, making a face. "He says Father was one of his best pupils. So I have a lot to live up to."

"We all have something to live up to," Jemmy said. "George Washington went to school here, too."

Dr. Campbell rapped on his desk, and the lessons began. After a while Jemmy noticed the other new boy, sitting across the aisle. He was small and palefaced. He didn't look very strong. He kept his eyes on Dr. Campbell all the time he spoke. It was plain to see that this boy had come here to learn.

At last Dr. Campbell paused. "It is time for recess," he said. "Go out and play for a while."

John Marshall got to his feet and stretched. "I've never sat still for so long in my life," he told Jemmy. "Father and Mother taught me at home. I could get up and go whenever I wished."

John and Jemmy went outside together. They stood at the top of the steps and looked around. A big field had been cleared of stumps and sowed to grass. This was where the boys played.

Jemmy pointed to a far corner of the field. Some big boys were standing around the small boy who had sat across the aisle from Jemmy. They had crowded him against the "snake-fence," or split rail fence, that went around the

field. The small boy looked pale, but not frightened. He stood his ground courageously.

"I hate bullies!" Jemmy said. "Let's go."

He and John crossed the field. They pushed
their way through the group of boys. Jemmy
doubled up his fists, ready to fight. But John put
his hand on the small boy's shoulder.

"Come along," he said. "We're getting up
some races and want you to be one of the judges."
He looked around at the other boys. "Any ob-
jections?" he asked. He stood head and shoulders above most of them. They drew back.

"None," their leader said. "When are the races
going to be held?"

"Now," John said. "Who wants to race me?"

"I do! I do! I do!" several boys cried at once.

"How about you, Jemmy?" asked John.

"I'll watch this time," Jemmy said. He went
over and stood beside the small boy, who said his
name was Tom Sullivan.

A few minutes later the boys were lined up, ready for the race.

"Three times around the field," John Marshall told them. "Is that all right?"

He slipped off his shoes and took his place. "I can run better in my stocking feet," he said. "Jemmy, you start us off."

"One—two—three—go!" Jemmy cried.

The runners took off. John led from the beginning. He was wearing stockings with blue tops and white feet, which his mother had knit.

It seemed to Jemmy that those white feet hardly touched the ground. In a short time John outdistanced everyone.

"He should be called Silver Heels," Tom Sullivan said. "The other runners see nothing but his white heels."

After that, every boy in Parson Campbell's school called John Silver Heels.

When school ended that day, Jemmy was almost sorry. He had made two good friends, John Marshall and Tom Sullivan.

John walked part way home with Jemmy. A handsome coach called for Tom. He was spending the winter with his grandparents. They lived too far from the school for Tom to walk. He stuck his head out the window of the coach. "Can't I drop you off somewhere?" he asked.

"Not today, thank you," said Jemmy. "I want to hunt. Sele, our cook, wants to make a pigeon pie. I promised I'd bring her some pigeons."

"I'll walk with Jemmy, thank you," said John. "I need some exercise."

"He's a nice fellow," John said as Tom rode off in the coach.

"He's little, but he's two years older than I am," Jemmy said. "Remember when Dr. Campbell asked for the dates of our births? Tom said he was born in 1756. I was born in 1758."

"I was born in 1755, so that makes you the youngest and me the oldest," John said. He laughed, then added a little sadly, "I've always been the oldest. I'm the oldest child in our family. I'm always expected to set an example for the others. Sometimes I wish somebody else would set the example for a change."

"So do I," Jemmy sighed. "I have to set an example for my younger brothers, too."

Boundary Lines

"John and I are going to see Black Feather," Jemmy told his mother one day a few weeks later. He had brought John Marshall home to spend the week end. John grew tired of staying at Parson Campbell's all the time.

The boys put their books in Jemmy's room and ran outdoors. They found the crisp November air pleasant after being cooped up.

"I'll race you!" John cried. Jemmy laughed good-naturedly. John always beat him. He hadn't been nicknamed Silver Heels for nothing. Jemmy didn't mind racing with him, but he didn't have much chance of winning.

The boys were out of breath when they reached Black Feather's small hut. Black Feather and a white man were standing before the door. As the boys drew near, they heard the white man speaking angrily. "If I catch you setting traps on my land again, I'll get the sheriff after you!"

"That's Mr. Hitchcock!" Jemmy exclaimed. "Let's find out what's wrong." The boys hurried forward. "What's the trouble, Mr. Hitchcock?" Jemmy asked.

"I found Black Feather setting traps on my land," Mr. Hitchcock said. "I just warned him to keep off."

"That Indian land," Black Feather said.

"All of it used to belong to your tribe, Black Feather," Jemmy said. "But you know the King of England owns it now. He gives or sells it to the settlers who come to America."

"Land still belong to Indians," Black Feather said stubbornly.

"I tell you that land belongs to me!" Mr. Hitchcock repeated. "I have nothing against you, Black Feather. You helped find my daughter and I haven't forgotten it. But I'll not let anybody fish or trap on my land, not even you."

He stalked away. A moment later he turned and shouted, "I'll get the sheriff after anyone who does. So just remember!"

"He seems to mean what he says," John said. "How much land does he own?"

"I don't know," Jemmy said. "His place isn't large. Some of it is here by the river." He turned to Black Feather. "You'd better be careful, Black Feather. He could make trouble for you if you've really trapped on his land."

"Me hunt and trap on Indian land," Black Feather repeated. "This all belong to Indian. White man not own land at all."

"Show us where he caught you," Jemmy said.

Black Feather started off. "Come! I show!" he said. "Not far away."

He went on ahead of the boys. Jemmy's legs were almost as long as Black Feather's now, and he didn't have any trouble keeping up.

"Here," Black Feather said at last. "This not white man's land."

"Can you prove it?" John Marshall asked.

"Not have to." With that Black Feather disappeared into the forest.

Suddenly Jemmy said, "I know what we can

144

do. We can check Mr. Hitchcock's boundary lines. I went with Father last spring when he checked ours. All we have to do is find Mr. Hitchcock's markers. Then we'd know whether Black Feather is right or not. Of course, the land wouldn't actually belong to the Indians. But it may not belong to Mr. Hitchcock, either."

"That's a good idea," John said. "Let's go."

It was hard work finding one of Mr. Hitchcock's markers. The swampy land near Black Feather's hut made walking hard, and the forest was not much better. But the boys kept at it.

Jemmy was the first to find something, a tree blazed with an axe. A blaze was a place where the bark had been chopped off the tree.

"Here's one!" he shouted.

"Good!" John said. "The rest will be fairly easy. We can pace it off from here. I've helped Father do it at home. Come on, I'll show you." John put his long legs into action.

The boys looked for other blazed trees. Some were easy to find, others hard. They worked their way from one marker to the next. At last they were back to the first one. They had walked all the way around Mr. Hitchcock's property.

"Black Feather was right!" Jemmy cried. "He wasn't trapping on Mr. Hitchcock's land after all! Let's go tell Mr. Hitchcock."

Mr. Hitchcock was angry when the two boys appeared at his door. "What now?" he demanded. "Are you still prying into my business?"

"We came to tell you Black Feather was right," Jemmy said. "He wasn't on your land."

"So you two schoolboys think you can tell me what I own!" Mr. Hitchcock exclaimed.

"Yes, sir," Jemmy said. "We can. We found your markers, and we paced off your land."

"What are you talking about?" Mr. Hitchcock demanded angrily.

"The boundary markers of your property, sir," Jemmy said. "John knew how to trace them. We found one of your marked trees and traced the rest from that one."

For a moment Mr. Hitchcock had nothing to say. He was both puzzled and angry. Then he snapped, "I know what I bought. That's my land, and that Indian had better stop trapping on it." With that, he shut the door.

"There's something odd about all this," John said. "I don't think he knows he's wrong."

"I don't know," Jemmy said. "He doesn't like Indians very well. Maybe that has something to do with it." He told John about the time Anne was lost. He told how Black Feather had helped to find her and bring her home.

"Mr. Hitchcock thought Black Feather had stolen Anne," Jemmy went on. "Black Feather was insulted."

"I think Black Feather had better hunt and

trap somewhere else," John said, "at least as long as Mr. Hitchcock thinks that land is his. You can't hunt or trap on someone else's property."

The next afternoon the family had just sat down to dinner when there was a knock on the door. Mr. Monroe was carving a turkey which the boys had shot.

At the sound of the knock, Mr. Monroe lifted his head. Mr. Hitchcock stood in the doorway.

"Come in," said Mrs. Monroe. "You're just in time for dinner. Jemmy, get Mr. Hitchcock a chair."

"Thank you, I've had my dinner," Mr. Hitchcock said. "I came to tell the boys they are right. Black Feather hasn't been trapping on my land. I traced the markers this morning."

He turned to the boys. "When I bought my place from Henry Anderson, he showed me some land that he said was his. He showed me the place where I caught Black Feather. I supposed

148

that he told me the truth. I never took time to find out for sure. So now I've come to tell you boys I'm sorry I lost my temper."

"That's all right," Jemmy said politely. "I'm glad you know we were right."

After drinking a cup of tea, Mr. Hitchcock left.

"He'd be a nice man if he didn't always jump to conclusions," Jemmy said.

Mr. Monroe wanted to know what had happened. "You boys did a good job," he said when they had told him. "I see you listen to your fathers, after all. Sometimes we wonder."

Jemmy and John grinned.

"What do you plan to do when you grow up?" Mrs. Monroe asked John. "Jemmy wants to study law. I think he would make a good ambassador." She smiled. "He's good at getting along with people."

"I'm going to be a lawyer, too," John told her.

"I think John would make a good judge,"

Jemmy said. "He always sees both sides of a question."

Jemmy started to push back his chair. "May we be excused?" he asked. "We want to tell Black Feather what Mr. Hitchcock just told us."

Black Feather didn't recognize Jemmy and John at a distance. He rushed from his hut, shouting and waving his arms.

"It's Jemmy, Black Feather," shouted Jemmy. "We've come to tell you Mr. Hitchcock doesn't own that land. You can hunt and trap there all you like."

"Black Feather told him it was Indian land," Black Feather said. "All land belong to Indian."

John and Jemmy looked at each other. Jemmy shook his head. "You'll never get him to admit the Indians don't own this land," he said.

JEMMY walked slowly along Duke of Gloucester Street in Williamsburg, the capital of Virginia. It was a warm October day in 1774. Jemmy was sixteen. He had been a student at the College of William and Mary for two weeks.

Duke of Gloucester Street was the main street in Williamsburg, and the busiest. Handsome coaches passed up and down, drawn by four or five horses. Farm wagons rumbled along with meats and vegetables for the markets. Men on horseback trotted up and down. Dust hung in the air long after the coaches and wagons and horses had passed.

he dust made Jemmy sneeze, but he didn't
e. Duke of Gloucester Street was surely the
est street in the world. There were so many
houses, so many shops!

He never tired of admiring the neat wooden
houses with their broad brick chimneys. He
never tired of looking in the shop windows.

As he walked along, he came to the shop of
a printer and bookbinder. He stopped to look
in the window. Suddenly he heard someone
calling, "Jemmy! Jemmy Monroe!"

Jemmy turned quickly. It was Harry Lee.
Harry sprang up the two steps that led to the
shop. He pounded Jemmy on the back. "It's
good to see you!" he exclaimed.

Jemmy was as glad to see Harry as Harry was
to see him. The boys sat down on a wooden
bench in front of the shop. It had been some
time since they had seen each other. So they had
many things to talk about.

At last the bells in Bruton Parish Church rang three times. "I'm meeting Cousin Richard for dinner," Harry said. "Why don't you come along? He'll be delighted to see you."

They walked down the street to the Raleigh Tavern. Harry led the way into the Apollo Room. There, planters and merchants sat at the sturdy tables.

Everyone seemed to be talking about the colonies' troubles with England. Parliament had repealed the Stamp Act eight years ago, but that had not ended the troubles. Now Parliament had passed another law that angered the colonists. This law was about tea, a simple little thing like tea.

There was already a tax on tea, but it was not heavy. However, the new law permitted an English company to sell tea more cheaply in the colonies than American merchants could.

The colonists thought such a law was unfair.

Some of them refused to drink tea. Others refused to buy tea. When the company's first tea ship reached Boston in December, 1773, trouble broke out. A group of colonists disguised themselves as Indians. They rowed out to the ship and went on board. They dumped the tea into the bay.

News of this "tea party" spread rapidly through the colonies. Patriots like Jemmy's father and Richard Henry Lee rejoiced. The Governors and other friends of Parliament and the King were angry.

Months had passed since the "Boston Tea Party," but people were angrier than ever. Colonists living in seaports refused to allow ships to unload tea. In one place, at least, angry citizens had burned a ship.

The boys stood in the doorway of the Apollo Room, listening to the excited talk. In a few minutes Mr. Richard Henry Lee saw them and called them to his table. Three men were already seated there with him.

Jemmy caught his breath. One of the men was Colonel Washington. Another was Patrick Henry. Jemmy hadn't seen either of them in many years. The third man was a stranger—tall, redheaded and freckled.

Richard Henry Lee placed Jemmy beside the stranger. "This is James Monroe," he said. "Jemmy, this is Mr. Thomas Jefferson."

Mr. Jefferson gave Jemmy a keen look and held out his hand. "I'm glad to meet you," he said. "Mr. Lee tells me you're attending my old school, the College of William and Mary."

"This young man had a hand in our meeting at Leedstown some years ago," Patrick Henry said with a smile.

"I remember him, too," Colonel Washington said. "I came across him one dark night on a trail in Westmoreland County. We both liked fast horses, I recall. I hope your father is well."

Jemmy blushed. He was surprised that important men like these remembered him. He didn't say much during dinner. He just listened.

Patrick Henry was especially interesting. He still had the smooth, powerful voice that Jemmy remembered. He still had much to say, too.

"Cousin Richard, Mr. Henry and Colonel Washington have just returned from Philadelphia," Harry told Jemmy. "They represented

Virginia in the Continental Congress that was held there a few weeks ago."

"Your cousin and Colonel Washington and I have just been talking about it," Patrick Henry said. "There was quite an argument over what we should do, but our side finally won. We wrote several resolutions and sent them to Parliament and the King.

"In these resolutions, we objected to many of the laws Parliament has passed lately. We objected to having English soldiers living here at our expense."

"We also warned the colonies to prepare for war," George Washington said. "It is good advice. I feel as if the colonists are sitting on a keg of gunpowder. There may be an explosion soon."

At that moment there was a shout in the street. "The races are starting!" Harry cried. "Cousin Richard, do you mind if Jemmy and I leave? I'd like to see the races, wouldn't you, Jemmy?"

"Go ahead," Mr. Lee said. "Our solemn talk must be of little interest to you."

Jemmy followed Harry to the street, but he would rather have stayed inside. He was even more interested in government and the problems facing the country now than he had been before.

When he and Harry reached the street, however, he soon caught the crowd's enthusiasm. Many people were standing along Duke of Gloucester Street, waiting to see the race.

Down the street Jemmy could see six horses, ready to race. A man stood beside them, with one arm upraised. "One—two—three—go!" the man shouted, and the horses were off.

It was a close race, but a beautiful brown horse led from the start. Jemmy watched it cross the finish line. There was something familiar about the young man riding it. He looked closely as the youth rode to the judge's stand for his prize. Then suddenly Jemmy recognized him.

158

"Peter Francisco!" he shouted in amazement.

Jemmy rushed forward and grasped Peter's hand. Jemmy was six feet tall now, but he had to look up to see Peter's face. Peter had become a giant! When he let go of Jemmy's hand, Jemmy shook it carefully as if it hurt. Peter laughed.

"I'm not that strong," he said.

"You could probably carry your horse better than it could carry you," Jemmy said jokingly.

Peter laughed again. "Well, I've never tried that," he said, "but I can do this." He walked over to a wagon standing at the side of the street. He leaned over and took hold of the rear end of the wagon. He lifted it until both rear wheels were a foot or so off the ground. "This is good exercise," he smiled as he let the wagon down again. "It gives me an appetite."

"Wonderful!" Harry cried. "You *are* a giant."

"You're a good rider, too," Jemmy said. "That's a beautiful horse, Peter."

160

Peter looked at his horse proudly. He went over and stroked her nose. "I raised her from a colt," he said. "Her name is White Star."

White Star was a good name, the boys agreed. The horse was a rich brown, with four white feet and a white star on her forehead.

The three boys went back to the Raleigh Tavern. By now the crowd was thinning out. Dust had settled in the street. The sun was sinking low in the west. Richard Henry Lee and his guests had gone.

"What shall we do now?" Harry asked.

"I know what I'd like to do," Peter said. "I'd like to see Jemmy's room at the college. I've always wanted to go to college, but I haven't been able to. To tell you the truth," he went on sadly, "I don't have much education at all."

"Why, Peter, how can that be possible?" Jemmy cried. "Surely Judge Winston could have sent you to school somewhere!"

Peter shrugged. "We were a long way from schools, and there were no other boys near by," he said. "The Judge taught me what he could, but he was busy. He didn't have much time."

For a moment the boys walked in silence out Duke of Gloucester Street. Then Peter said, "War is coming soon, I think. Already there is talk of it. Congress even advised the colonies to prepare. If it comes, I'll join the army."

"So will I," Jemmy said.

"And I," said Harry Lee.

Peter was delighted with Jemmy's room. His dark eyes shone as he looked at the bed, the desk and Jemmy's books. "Here's something, Peter," Jemmy said, handing him a globe. "Here's where you came from." He pointed to Spain and Portugal in southwestern Europe.

Peter traced a line from Spain to Virginia. "I came a long way," he said with a thoughtful look. Then he smiled, "You know, I'm glad I'm here!"

"Good for you, Peter!" Jemmy cried. "I feel the same way. There's not a country in the world better than our own."

The three boys walked back to the Raleigh Tavern, where Harry and Peter were staying. Then Jemmy returned to his room. He thought of all that had happened that day. He thought of Colonel Washington and Patrick Henry. He thought of Thomas Jefferson, whose friendly, easy way he had liked at once. He thought of what they had said, and what Peter had said. Yes, trouble was coming, perhaps war. Jemmy was glad there were such men as George Washington and Patrick Henry and Thomas Jefferson. They would watch over the country's safety when trouble came.

Old Friends
Meet Again

IT WAS a cold March day in the year 1821. A strong wind drove sleet down the muddy streets of Washington, D.C. In one room of the White House were the President of the United States, the members of his Cabinet and his wife, Elizabeth. The President's name was James Monroe.

"You look very handsome," Mrs. Monroe said, smiling at her husband.

The President—still Jemmy or Jim to his friends—turned to study himself carefully in a long mirror. He was wearing a black broadcloth suit with silver buttons. There were gold buckles on his shoes. Buttons and buckles had been polished until they shone. Faithful Ralph had worked hard on them.

Satisfied with his appearance, the President ran his hand over his graying hair. It was long and tied at the back of his neck with a narrow black ribbon. He smiled at his wife.

"Thank you, my dear," he said. "Ralph says we should start for the Capitol early. So if you will excuse me, I'll go on ahead."

"Of course," Mrs. Monroe said. "It certainly wouldn't do for the President of the United States to be late for his second inauguration."

"The people really seemed to want me for a second term, didn't they?" Jemmy said. "I still find that very hard to believe."

"Almost everyone voted for you," said Mrs. Monroe proudly. "You were the favorite."

"Be sure to wrap up well," Jemmy said as he kissed Elizabeth good-by. "It's a bad day and I don't want you to catch a cold."

Elizabeth laughed. "You would think of my comfort on a day like this!"

Jemmy went outside, followed by the members of his Cabinet. Ralph was sitting on the front seat of the modest carriage that waited before the door. He was to ride with Jemmy to the Capitol. He wanted to make sure that Mr. Jemmy looked right when he took the oath of office as President.

Jemmy stepped into the carriage. The driver whipped up his horses, and off they went. The Cabinet members followed in other carriages.

In spite of the weather there were many people in the streets. They cheered the President's carriage as it rolled by. Jemmy smiled and bowed to right and left. When they reached the Capitol, he glanced at his watch. He was a half hour early.

A committee of senators and congressmen met him at the door and led him to a private room. "Chief Justice Marshall is already here," one senator said as he opened the door.

Jemmy entered the room. "Well, John, it's good to see you," he said. He crossed the room with his hand stretched out.

A tall, rangy figure rose and bowed. "Thank you, Mr. President," he said.

"Don't call me that, John," Jemmy begged. "I hope I'll always be Jemmy to you and my other

167

old friends. I'm not going to address you as 'Mr. Chief Justice,' even if you are the highest judge in the land."

John Marshall laughed. "You haven't changed much, Jemmy. Even four years as President haven't changed you very much, I'm glad to say."

"Why should I change?" Jemmy asked simply. "Merely being President doesn't make me better than anyone else." He pushed forward a comfortable chair and took a smaller one close to it. "Sit down," he added. "We have several minutes yet."

After they were seated, they were silent for a short while. Then Jemmy said, "It seems a long time since we were in Parson Campbell's school, doesn't it? We had a good time there."

"Yes," John said. "But I never would have thought then that I was going to school with a future President of the United States."

Jemmy laughed. "I never thought you'd be

Chief Justice of the United States Supreme Court, either. How could I? How could you? Such offices didn't exist then. There wasn't even a United States. I can remember, though, that you always could see both sides of a question."

"How many years have passed since then!" John said. "Many things have happened."

"Yes. They've been eventful years," Jemmy agreed. He began to laugh. "Do you remember when you came to Williamsburg while I was in college? What a sight you and those Minute Men of yours were!"

John Marshall smiled as he recalled that day. War had been close then, and he was commanding a company of Minute Men from the frontier. They were on their way north to join General Washington and his army.

"What a wild-looking lot you were!" Jemmy said. "Do you know you scared the good people of Williamsburg? They weren't used to frontiersmen. Those green uniforms and buck-tailed hats and scalping knives were frightening."

John shook his head. "There weren't a half dozen of us who knew what was ahead," he said. "We learned, though, and quickly."

They had both been young when the fighting started, but they had joined the army. They had been at Valley Forge that cold winter when the country's future seemed so uncertain. Jemmy had been at the Battle of Trenton, too. He had been wounded there and for some time afterward had been an invalid. Even now his shoulder bothered him on cold days like this.

"I wonder what would have happened if we hadn't had General Washington," said Jemmy.

"We would have had no country," John answered promptly. "He held us together by the strength of his will."

Both men fell silent again. Jemmy looked at his watch. It was almost time.

"Whatever became of Peter Francisco?" John asked. "You knew him, didn't you?"

"Yes, indeed—Peter Francisco, the Virginia Giant," answered Jemmy. "He made quite a name for himself during the war, you know. Six feet, six inches tall, and all man! He was so big that General Washington had a special five-foot sword made for him."

Jemmy smiled. "I've heard that he pulled a cannon once all by himself, after the horses had been killed. I can believe it. I saw him lift a a wagon once myself. That was in Williamsburg, shortly before the war."

"Harry Lee was a fine soldier, too," John said. "He was a popular cavalry officer. His men gave him his nickname, Light-Horse Harry. He is a great friend of yours, isn't he?"

"Yes, indeed," said Jemmy fondly. "Harry is living at Stratford Hall now. I wish he were still in Congress. I could use his help."

There was a knock on the door. "Come in," Jemmy said. The door opened halfway, and Ralph's head appeared.

"They're about ready, Mr. President. I came to see that you look right." He entered the room and looked Jemmy over from head to foot. He straightened a fold in Jemmy's coat and polished the silver buttons once more. Then he stepped back. "All right, Mr. President," he said. "You can go."

Arm in arm, James Monroe and John Marshall left the room. They went to the large hall where the ceremony would be held. Many people were gathered in the hall. There were senators and representatives from all the states. There were ambassadors from other countries. Jemmy saw Peter Francisco in the background, towering over everyone else. Jemmy smiled. He was glad to see his old friend. There would be a good talk later in the day, he knew.

"I wish Mr. Jefferson could have come," said Jemmy. "But he doesn't leave his home at Monticello much these days. It's a long trip from his home to Washington."

"Didn't you live near him once?" John asked.

"Yes, Mr. Jefferson designed a place for me not far from Monticello. It wasn't large, but I liked it. I hated to sell it.

"However, I had to be nearer Washington, so I built Oak Hill. My wife and daughters think there is no place like Oak Hill. I like it, too, but I miss my visits to Monticello. Mr. Jefferson has been a good friend to me."

John Marshall chuckled. "He and I don't agree on many things, you know."

"He is the best friend a man could have," Jemmy said simply. "I studied law under him after the war. There never was a better or more patient teacher. I have much to thank him for. We have been close friends for years."

"I heard him say something about you once. He said, 'James Monroe is a man whose soul might be turned wrong side outwards without discovering a blemish to the world.'"

Jemmy smiled. "It was his faith in me that kept me going. He always believed in me."

"We must take our places now," John said.

The two tall gray-haired men entered the hall of the House of Representatives. They stood before the solemn crowd. Somebody put a Bible on the stand in front of them. James Monroe, President of the United States of America, placed his hand on it. He looked confidently into the dark eyes of his old friend as he took the oath of office for the second time.

A Birthday Celebration

ONE EVENING early in April, 1958, the Wilson family was watching a news program on television. "Plans are being completed for a celebration on James Monroe's two hundredth birthday," said the reporter. "It will be held on April twenty-eighth, at Montross, Virginia."

"Montross!" exclaimed Mrs. Wilson. "Why, that's not more than a hundred miles from here. I think we should go to the celebration."

"I read something about it in my stamp magazine," said Charles. He was eleven years old and an eager stamp collector. "A special three-cent stamp is being printed in honor of James Monroe. The new stamp will be shown for the first time at the celebration."

"I'd like to go," said nine-year-old Susan. Susan loved to travel. She always was ready to go anywhere at any time.

"Then I guess we'd all like to go," said Mr. Wilson. "I know that I would."

The next evening Mr. Wilson was reading the paper before dinner. "Here's an article about the celebration," he said. "Many important people are planning to be there. The Ambassador from Brazil is to be the main speaker on the program."

Susan was setting the table. When she heard her father, she ran into the living room with her hands full of silverware.

"Brazil is in South America," she said. "Why should a South American be the speaker?"

"It's a little hard to explain," said Mr. Wilson, "but I'll try."

He thought for a moment. Then he began. "The people of South America remember that James Monroe helped their countries to become independent. While he was President, he told European countries to keep out of the affairs of American countries. The warning that he wrote is called the Monroe Doctrine."

Charles had learned about the Monroe Doctrine in school. He said, "The Monroe Doctrine really says that America is for Americans, doesn't it, Dad?"

"That's the main idea," Mr. Wilson replied. "James Monroe also wanted all the American countries to be good neighbors, and they have been. That is why a man from South America is going to speak at the celebration."

"Susan," called Mrs. Wilson from the kitchen. "Have you finished setting the table?"

"Almost," said Susan, hurrying back to the dining room. "I'll be through in a minute."

A few days later Charles came home from school with an armful of books. "Hello, Mom," he said as he put the books on the table. "Guess what happened in school today."

"I'm not a good guesser," Mrs. Wilson said.

"Well, I told my teacher that we are going to the celebration at Montross," said Charles. "She thought it would be a good idea if I learned more about Monroe before we go."

"Oh, that *is* a good idea," Mrs. Wilson smiled.

"Anyway," Charles went on, "I wound up by offering to give a report on his life in class."

"So that's why you brought all those books home with you," said Mrs. Wilson.

"Yes," Charles nodded. "You and Dad and Susan are going to the celebration, too. I thought you might like to read about Monroe."

"Chiefly you thought that we might help you with your report," Mrs. Wilson teased.

"I could use some help on deciding what to

put into it," Charles admitted. "Monroe did so many things, I hardly know where to start."

"The usual way to start the story of a person's life is to tell when and where he was born," said Mrs. Wilson.

"Oh, I know those things," Charles said. "James Monroe was born on a plantation in Westmoreland County, April twenty-eighth, 1758. The plantation was near Montross."

"That's why the celebration is being held at Montross," said Mrs. Wilson.

"He lived on the plantation until he was sixteen," Charles went on. "Then he went to college. I need help on selecting the most important things that he did later in his life."

After dinner each member of the family took one of the books that Charles had brought home. Susan chose the one with the most pictures.

"You know what to say about the first sixteen years of James Monroe's life, Charles," said Mrs.

180

Wilson. "But you want to know what to include from that time on. Is that right?"

"Yes," Charles nodded. "Do you think it is important that he left college after two years and joined the Continental Army?"

"I do," said Mr. Wilson. "He was a fine soldier during the Revolutionary War."

"This book says that he left the army in 1780 to study law," Mrs. Wilson said. "I think you should mention that he was a lawyer."

"He was elected to the Virginia Assembly when he was only twenty-four years old," Mr. Wilson said.

"What was that?" Susan asked.

"It was a group of men who made Virginia's laws," Mr. Wilson explained. "In early days, the lawmaking group was called the House of Burgesses. Later it was the Virginia Assembly."

"Here's something," said Charles, looking up from his book. "Monroe was a member of the

181

Congress that was elected after the Revolutionary War. This Congress met before the United States had a President. It provided the first real government that the United States had."

"I think something about Monroe's family would be interesting," Susan said.

"While he was in Congress, he met and married a young lady named Elizabeth Kortright," said Mrs. Wilson. "They had two daughters, whose names were Elizabeth and Maria."

"That reminds me," Mr. Wilson said. "I heard today that a great-great-grandson of James Monroe is going to be at the celebration."

"Shall I put that in?" asked Charles.

Mr. Wilson laughed. "No, that would be getting ahead of your story. I just happened to think of it when Susan mentioned the family."

"Probably the next thing would be that James Monroe and his wife moved to Fredericksburg," said Charles. "He practiced law there."

182

"His law office is still there," Mr. Wilson said. "It is a kind of museum now. I went through it once when I was on a vacation. I saw the gun and the sword that Monroe carried during the Revolutionary War. I saw the desk that he used when he signed the Monroe Doctrine."

"I wish we could go there some time," said Susan. "I'd like to see the museum."

"Perhaps we can," Mr. Wilson said. "Now,

back to the report. The Monroes moved from Fredericksburg to Charlottesville. Thomas Jefferson designed a house for them."

"I've seen that house," Mrs. Wilson exclaimed. "It's called Ash Lawn now, but it didn't have a name when the Monroes lived there. It's near Jefferson's home, Monticello, a few miles away, across the hills."

"James Monroe and Thomas Jefferson must have been good friends," said Charles.

"They were," Mr. Wilson agreed. "Jefferson's friendship was one of the most important things in Monroe's life."

Charles was reading again. "When Thomas Jefferson was President, he sent James Monroe to France. I think that's important."

"It was very important to the United States," said Mr. Wilson. "Monroe was one of the men who arranged to have the United States buy the Louisiana Territory from France.

"Of course," Mr. Wilson explained, "Louisiana Territory was quite different from Louisiana today. It took in most of the land between the Mississippi River and the Rocky Mountains."

"In one way or another, Monroe had a lot to do with the growth of the United States, didn't he?" Mrs. Wilson asked. "Later, when he was President, he bought Florida from Spain."

"Before he was elected President in 1816, he was the Governor of Virginia," Charles said.

"He was Secretary of State when Madison was President and, for a while, Secretary of War."

"He was one of our best Presidents," Mrs. Wilson said. "He did many things for the people. Two of the things are not well known, but they show clearly the kind of man he was.

"As President, he approved a plan for setting up an Indian Territory in the West. He wanted the Indians to have this land for a permanent home. Presidents who came after him didn't adopt his plan, and his dream never came true.

"His other dream was more successful. He wanted to create a new home for Negro slaves. He disliked slavery and worked to set up a colony in Africa, called Liberia. Freed slaves went there to live in a new country of their own. Today Liberia is a thriving republic. Its capital is called Monrovia in honor of Monroe."

Susan was getting restless. "How much longer is this report going to be?" she asked.

"Not very much," Charles answered. "I think I'll just add that James Monroe died on the Fourth of July in 1831."

Charles gathered up the notes he had made. "Thanks," he said. "I think I know now what I want to put into my report."

On the twenty-eighth of April, the Wilsons drove to Montross. They went directly to the Courthouse Green, where the celebration was to be held.

A speakers' stand had been placed on the steps of the courthouse. In front of it were rows of chairs. A crowd was beginning to gather, but the Wilsons were early. They had no trouble finding good seats. The first two rows of chairs were being kept for the speakers and the guests.

It was a gray day, but the Courthouse Green was bright with color. The redbud and dogwood trees were in blossom, and many spring flowers were in bloom.

There was more color to come. Before long a Marine Corps Band came marching and playing across the Green. The men were wearing their red and blue dress uniforms.

Then came some young men, carrying flags of many different colors. The United States flag was first. Behind it were flags from all the other countries in the Western Hemisphere. The flag bearers placed the flags in a row at the back of the speakers' stand.

Finally the people who were to sit in the first two rows arrived. Among them were the Deputy Postmaster General of the United States and the mayor of Montross. Also there were Laurence G. Hoes, the great-great-grandson of James Monroe, and his wife. There were ambassadors from all the Latin-American countries. Most of these men had brought their wives with them.

When the band stopped playing, the mayor of Montross climbed the steps to the speakers' stand. He welcomed all the people, then introduced Mr. Hoes. Mr. Hoes made a short speech, introducing the Brazilian Ambassador.

The Ambassador from Brazil said, in part, "For more than a century Brazil and the United States have been close friends. President James Monroe, whom we have come today to honor, is the symbol of all that is finest in that relationship. It was while he was President that the United States recognized the independence of my country."

The Deputy Postmaster General spoke next. Toward the end of his speech, the postmaster of Montross went up to the speakers' stand. The Deputy Postmaster General held up an album of special three-cent stamps that had been printed in honor of James Monroe.

Charles wished that he were close enough to see what the new stamp looked like. But he would have to wait until the program was over.

190

"A helicopter is waiting now to take the postmaster to Washington," said the Deputy Postmaster General. "He is going to deliver these stamps to President Eisenhower."

The local postmaster took the album and hurried away as people clapped and cheered. In a few minutes, the crowd saw the helicopter rise into the air. The postmaster was on his way.

"I wish I could fly in a helicopter," Susan said. "I'd like to go to Washington."

The program was over now, and the crowd began to leave. Everyone was talking about James Monroe and what a great man he was.

Charles bought some of the new stamps for his collection. He also addressed several first day cover envelopes to himself. They would arrive through the mail in a day or two.

Late in the afternoon the Wilsons started home. "James Monroe must have loved his country," Charles said.

"He did," Mr. Wilson agreed. "He loved it deeply. He died a poor man because he had spent his life working for his country. He was so busy with affairs of government that he never had time to make much money for himself."

"You know," Susan said, "I've learned so much about James Monroe that I feel as if I know him. He seems like a good friend."

"You couldn't have a better one," said Mrs. Wilson. "Monroe was a good friend and neighbor to everyone. He was truly a great American."

DO YOU REMEMBER?

1. When and where was James Monroe born?
2. Where did Jemmy go for help when his father was bitten by a snake?
3. Why did Jemmy and Ralph become frightened when they went to the woodpile?
4. What new friend did Jemmy meet when he went to watch the ship unload?
5. What happened to Jemmy and Ralph when they tried to find Anne Hitchcock?
6. Who was Mr. Douglas and why did he come to live with the Monroe family?
7. What kind of animal did Jemmy kill on the way home from the fox hunt?
8. How did Ralph win a hat at Stratford Hall?
9. Why did Jemmy and Harry hide Mickey Cook in the attic at Stratford Hall?
10. Who were Jemmy's closest friends while he attended Parson Campbell's school?
11. How did Jemmy and John settle an argument between Black Feather and Mr. Hitchcock?
12. Where did Jemmy go to college?

13. Why did the colonies have trouble with England?

14. What did Monroe do during the Revolutionary War?

15. What occupation did he follow after the war?

16. What different government positions did he hold before he became President?

17. Why did he issue his famous statement called the Monroe Doctrine?

18. How did he help to enlarge our country?

IMPORTANT THINGS TO LOOK UP

1. What was the Stamp Act and why did the colonies so strongly oppose it?

2. What was the First Continental Congress and why did it meet?

3. How did each of the following men mentioned in the story help to establish our country: John Marshall, Thomas Jefferson, Richard Henry Lee, Patrick Henry?

4. Why is the period when Monroe was President often called the "Era of Good Feeling"?

5. Where is the city of Williamsburg and why do many tourists go there today?

INTERESTING THINGS TO DO

1. Draw a map of the part of Virginia where Jemmy grew up and show where you think the following places were: Potomac River, Rappahannock River, Monroe Creek, Monroe plantation.

2. Find out why these homes mentioned in the story are famous: Monroe Hall, Stratford Hall, Oak Hill, Wakefield, Ash Lawn, Monticello.

3. Make a drawing of a stagecoach, such as people used in Monroe's day, and place it on the bulletin board for others to see.

4. Pretend that you made a trip to Williamsburg in Monroe's time and write a short story about things you saw there.

5. Prepare a list of things that Monroe did while he was President and explain why each was helpful to our country or the world.

OTHER BOOKS TO READ

American Revolution, The. Bruce Bliven, Jr., Trade Edition, Random House. School Edition, Hale.

Louisiana Purchase, The, Robert Tallant. Trade Edition, Random House. School Edition, Hale.

Spy in Old Philadelphia, A, Anne Emery. Rand McNally.

Thomas Jefferson, Champion of the People, Clara Ingram Judson. Follett.

We Were There When Washington Won at Yorktown, Earl Schenck Miers. Grosset.

WHEN JAMES MONROE LIVED

1758 JAMES MONROE WAS BORN, APRIL 28.

The thirteen colonies were ruled by England.

The population of the colonies was about 1,600,000.

The French and Indian War ended, 1763.

Daniel Boone first went to Kentucky, 1769.

1770 JEMMY ATTENDED DR. CAMPBELL'S SCHOOL.

The "Boston Tea Party" took place, 1773.

The colonists objected to many English laws.

1774– JEMMY ATTENDED THE COLLEGE OF WILLIAM
1776   AND MARY.

First Continental Congress met, 1774.

Patrick Henry delivered his famous "liberty or death" speech, 1775.

The Battle of Lexington was fought, 1775.

1776– 1780	MONROE SERVED IN THE CONTINENTAL ARMY.

The Declaration of Independence was adopted, July 4, 1776.

General Burgoyne surrendered, 1777.

1780– 1782	MONROE STUDIED LAW UNDER THOMAS JEFFERSON.

Cornwallis was defeated at Guilford Court House, 1781.

Cornwallis surrendered at Yorktown, 1781.

1782– 1809	MONROE HELD MANY GOVERNMENT POSITIONS.

The peace treaty with England was signed, 1783.

The Constitutional Convention met to frame the United States Constitution, 1787.

George Washington was President, 1789–1797.

Eli Whitney invented the cotton gin, 1793.

John Adams was President, 1797–1801.

George Washington died, 1799.

Thomas Jefferson was President, 1801–1809.

Lewis and Clark explored the Northwest, 1804–1806.

James Madison became President, 1809.

1809–1817	MONROE SERVED AS SECRETARY OF STATE.
	The War of 1812 was fought, 1812–1815.
	"The Star-Spangled Banner" was written, 1814.
1817–1825	MONROE SERVED AS PRESIDENT.
	Florida was purchased from Spain, 1819.
	The first steamship crossed the Atlantic, 1819.
	The Monroe Doctrine was issued, 1823.
1831	JAMES MONROE DIED, JULY 4.
	There were 24 states in the Union.
	The population was about 13,000,000.
	Andrew Jackson was President.

HELP WITH WORDS

ambassador (ăm băs′à dẽr) : person sent to another country as the chief official representative of his own country

apologize: say one is sorry for an act

"Boston Tea Party": dumping of tea from English ships into Boston Harbor by colonists, disguised as Indians, 1773

cavalry (kăv′ăl rĭ) : branch of the army in which soldiers ride horses

198

College of William and Mary: one of the oldest colleges in the United States, founded in 1693

Continental Army (kŏn tĭ nĕn′tăl) : army that fought for American independence during the Revolutionary War

Continental Congress (kŏn tĭ nĕn′tăl kŏng′grĕs) : meeting of delegates or representatives from all the colonies, first held to discuss troubles with England, later to govern the united colonies

field hands: persons who worked in the fields on plantations, planting and harvesting crops

Henry, Patrick: American statesman from Virginia; one of the leading Revolutionary figures

hoecakes: cakes made from corn meal, once cooked in front of a fire on a hoe

House of Burgesses (bûr′jĕs ĕs) : lawmaking body of Virginia in colonial days

Jefferson, Thomas (jĕf′ẽr sŭn) : American statesman from Virginia; author of the Declaration of Independence; President of the United States, 1801–1809

Lafayette, Marquis de (lä′fȧ yĕt′ mär′kwĭs dē) : French nobleman who fought for the colonists during the Revolutionary War

Lee, Harry: cavalry general in the Revolutionary War, called Light-Horse Harry

Lee, Richard Henry: Revolutionary leader and signer of the Declaration of Independence

Marshall, John: first Chief Justice of the United States Supreme Court

minuet (mĭn′ū̇ ĕt′) : graceful dance popular in colonial days

Parliament (pär′lĭ mĕnt) : lawmaking body of the government of England

porridge (pŏr′ĭj) : cooked breakfast food, usually made of corn, wheat or oats

Raleigh Tavern (rô′lĭ tăv′ẽrn) : inn, or hotel, at Williamsburg in colonial days

resolutions (rĕz′ȯ lū′shŭnz) : statements telling the decisions reached by a group of persons

snuffbox: small box for holding snuff or powdered tobacco

Stamp Act: act passed by Parliament, which forced the colonists to buy stamps for documents, or official papers

sweetmeats: candies and candied fruits

Valley Forge (fôrj) : camp where George Washington and his army spent the winter of 1777–1778

Wakefield: plantation home of the Washington family, where George Washington was born

Williamsburg: capital of the colony of Virginia